ICRISAT Pigeonpea Germplasm Catalog: Evaluation and Analysis

P. Remanandan, D.V.S.S.R. Sastry, and Melak H. Mengesha

ICRISAT

International Crops Research Institute for the Semi-Arid Tropics
Patancheru, A.P. 502 324, India.

1988

Foreword

There is global awareness that future advancement in agriculture depends upon present efforts to conserve and enhance the world's plant genetic resources. Genetic resources work may not yield immediate and dramatic results, but the silent role it plays in the genetic improvement of crop plants is well recognized.

One of ICRISAT's long-term objectives is to serve as a world repository for the genetic resources of its mandate crops of which pigeonpea is one. The Genetic Resources Unit (GRU) collects germplasm from priority areas, and employs appropriate technology to maintain, evaluate, and document this material. A special effort is made to provide optimum seed storage conditions, and the germplasm is made freely available to scientists throughout the world.

The main users of the germplasm are the Institute's crop improvement scientists and the scientists of national institutes in countries of the semi-arid tropics (SAT). Scientists from 90 countries, mostly within the SAT, have to date drawn pigeonpea germplasm samples from the ICRISAT gene bank for utilization in national crop improvement programs.

The pigeonpea collection has now grown to 11 034 accessions from 50 countries. The efficiency of its utilization in crop improvement depends largely upon its diversity, viability, and its accessibility in a well-defined and classified form. This catalog presents the results of multidisciplinary efforts in germplasm evaluation, characterization, screening, and classification of the world collection of pigeonpea. The effort of the GRU staff in the development of this catalog is commendable and I encourage them to continue their good work.

However, this is not the end of the work on pigeonpea germplasm. ICRISAT must continue to assemble, conserve, evaluate, and document more invaluable landraces, so that they too are made available for utilization in present and future crop improvement programs throughout the world and particularly in the SAT.

This catalog presents classified and concise information on the present state of pigeonpea genetic resources. Its imaginative use will promote and accelerate pigeonpea germplasm enhancement and utilization.

L.D. Swindale
Director General

Preface

Pigeonpea is a unique crop with wide adaptability to diverse climates and soils. It is cultivated in most tropical and subtropical environments. The Indian subcontinent is the major area in which the crop evolved and diversified. Pigeonpea is now becoming increasingly important in many other areas such as Southeast Asia, Africa, Central America, and the Caribbean because it is useful as a source of food and fuel wood. Any improvement in its productivity will make an impact on rainfed agriculture in crop rotations.

In 1979 the International Workshop on Pigeonpea recognized the need and scope to expand pigeonpea production throughout the world. India, the principal cultivator of the crop also developed a strategy to increase production, but this did not happen at the required pace. Pigeonpea improvement is a real challenge, we still need to make a breakthrough.

For a systematic crop improvement program, germplasm is the basic material, and the key to success lies in the crop's genetic diversity. The variability present in pigeonpea is quite large, and this catalog presents results of comprehensive evaluation and screening carried out by ICRISAT over several years. An attempt has been made to create several natural and artificial groups, and to provide ready-to-use short lists of genotypes that breeders will find useful in their selection and hybridization programs.

The present collection conserved in the ICRISAT gene bank consists of traditional landraces with adequate geographical representation, purified lines, known sources of resistance to various biotic and abiotic stresses, improved cultivars, and wild relatives. The collection now serves as the genetic base for pigeonpea improvement at ICRISAT and throughout the world. ICRISAT scientist have used 52 236 samples over the years in various experiments. We have distributed 19 914 seed samples to centers in India, and 9067 samples to 90 other countries. To further stimulate and facilitate effective and expanded use, all the available data on passport information and evaluation are compiled into this catalog which is available in two volumes- Evaluation and Analysis and Passport Information. Based on feedback from the germplasm users, we will continue to revise and improve our records and these publications.

I know that it has taken much time and multidisciplinary effort to compile and produce these catalogs. It is a major achievement with which I am glad to be associated. The Genetic Resources Unit and all the scientists and staff of Information Services deserve to be congratulated on this commendable work.

J.S. Kanwar
Deputy Director General Emeritus

Acknowledgements

We are indebted to Dr L.D. Swindale, Director General, and Dr J.S. Kanwar, Deputy Director General Emeritus, of ICRISAT for their overall support and encouragement during the preparation of this catalog.

A large number of institutions and scientists cooperated with ICRISAT to assemble the world collection and carry out germplasm collection expeditions in various parts of the world. We have attempted to list the most important contributors on page 0. We acknowledge their generous assistance.

Evaluation at ICRISAT is carried out by multidisciplinary participation and the data presented in this catalog is the result of well coordinated and truely collaborative team work.

We gratefully acknowledge the contribution of Dr L.J.G. van der Maesen, Professor of Plant Taxonomy, University of Wageningen and Dr Anishetty N. Murthi, IBPGR, who were working on pigeonpea genetic resources at ICRISAT from 1975 to 1983 and 1974 to 1978 respectively.

Several scientists at ICRISAT reviewed this manuscript, and offered constructive criticism which helped us to improve the technical content and we are specially grateful to Drs W. Reed, D.G. Faris, Laxman Singh, C. Johansen, Murari Singh, K.B. Saxena, K.C. Jain, and M.V. Reddy.

We thank Dr J.W. Estes for guidance in documentation, Ms Nithi Devi Saxena for computer assistance, Mr G. Swaminathan for data analysis, and Ms Shoba for secretarial assistance. Finally we wish to express our appreciation to Information Services and particularly to Susan D. Hall, Research Editor, and B.J. Walby, Consultant Editor for editing and improving the style and presentation of the catalog.

The following past and present ICRISAT staff contributed to the assembly and evaluation of the pigeonpea germplasm.

Genetic Resources	Melak H. Mengesha, L.J.G. van der Maesen[1], Anishetty N. Murthi[1], P. Remanandan, D.V.S.S.R. Sastry, N. Kameshwara Rao, D. Krishnaiah, D.R. Pawar, V. Ramakrishna Reddy[1], C.S. Satish Chandra[1]
Pathology	Y.L. Nene, M.V. Reddy, M.P. Haware, A.M. Ghanekar, S.P.S. Beniwal[1], J. Kannaiyan[1], S.B. Sharma, K.M. Rao[1], B.C. Reddy[1], T.N. Raju, S.H. Mahamulkar[1], V.K. Sheila, E. Deena[1]
Entomology	W. Reed[1], S.S. Lateef, S. Sithanantham, G.R.B. Sastry[1], K.V. Prasad Rao, P. Rama Goud[1], V.R. Bhagwat, V. Rameshwar Rao, Y. Satyanarayana
Biochemistry	R. Jambunathan, Umaid Singh, P.V. Rao, G.L. Waghray, G. Venkateswarlu, G. Soma Raju
Breeding	J.M. Green[1], D.G. Faris, D. Sharma[1], Laxman Singh, L.J.Reddy, K.C. Jain, S.C. Gupta, K.B. Saxena, G.K. Bhatia[1]
Statistics	B. Gilliver, Murari Singh, G. Swaminathan, V.R. Prabhakar
Data processing	J.W. Estes, Nithi Devi Saxena[1], Lydia Flynn, M. Rita Grace, K. Chandrakala

1. Indicates no longer in ICRISAT service.

Contents

Introduction

One of ICRISAT's major objectives is to act as a world repository for the genetic resources of its mandate crops, of which pigeonpea (*Cajanus cajan* (L). Millsp.) is one. In 1978, the International Board for Plant Genetic Resources (IBPGR) requested that ICRISAT assume the responsibility of serving as the major repository for the germplasm of the Institute's five crops. ICRISAT accepted this responsibility and created the Genetic Resources Unit (GRU) on 1 January 1979 by incorporating the various crop germplasm activities of the institute into one coordinated unit. The Unit aims at enhancing ICRISAT's services as a world center for the improvement of the genetic potential of its crops. The major activities are collection, maintenance, conservation, evaluation, documentation, and distribution of the mandate crops — sorghum, pearl millet, chickpea, pigeonpea, and groundnut. The International Gene Bank maintained by GRU houses the largest collection of germplasm of these crops assembled at one place.

Pigeonpea is an important source of high-protein food in many countries in the semi-arid tropics. It performs well under marginal input and has the inherent ability to withstand some environmental stresses particularly drought. In recent years it has become one of the most sought after crops in plant introduction trials aimed at bringing new areas under cultivation. This is due to its ability to perform satisfactorily in harsh situations where most other crops do not survive.

India is considered to be the primary center of origin and diversification of pigeonpea (Fig. 1) (van der Maesen 1980). It is the second most important grain legume of India, after chickpea. Other important areas for its cultivation are East Africa, Caribbean Islands, parts of South and Central America, and South and Southeast Asia (Fig. 2). Its evolution under natural selection aided by man in a wide range of agroecological areas (Fig. 3) has resulted in numerous locally adapted landraces.

Pigeonpea improvement started in India in the 1920s and many improved lines have been developed since then. This, however, has not yet resulted in a substantial increase in total production. One major reason for this has been attributed to the limited use of the available germplasm (Ramanujam and Singh 1981). Compared to the major cereal crops, attempts to improve pigeonpea have been inadequate and it is expected that large genetic gains will be achieved rapidly if adequate attention is given (Byth et al. 1981). The key to success lies in the variability and potentiality of the crop's genetic resources (ICRISAT 1982b). The germplasm assembled at ICRISAT provide a wide range of variability (Table 1) in all agronomically important traits, particularly days to maturity, plant type, seed size, number of seeds per pod, and resistance to environmental and biotic stresses.

The importance of conserved germplasm depends in part on the genetic diversity it contains (Mengesha 1984). It is obvious from Table 1 that the genetic variation is very high and we have only just begun to exploit it (Byth 1981). So far the contribution of landraces as source material for improvement has been substantial. Almost all elite breeding lines are selections from traditional landraces (Table 2).

There are already examples of landraces collected from farmers' fields proving to be of value. For example Fiji recently released ICP 7035 for cultivation to farmers. Because of its high sugar content, the line has been named 'Kamica', which means sweet in Fijian. This line is a field collection from Madhya Pradesh, India. It combines multiple resistance against fusarium wilt and sterility mosaic with excellent vegetable-type characteristics and so is now being extensively used in the improvement of vegetable types. ICP 8863, a wilt resistant selection from ICRISAT, has been recently released in Karnataka, India with the popular name 'Maruti'. ICP 3193 is a widely used parental source in the breeding of lines tolerant to *Heliothis*.

The yield potential available in landraces is also remarkable. Many germplasm lines identified for high performance in earlier assessments have been utilized in breeding programs at ICRISAT and selections from ICP 8885, 9590, 10128, 9530, 8709, and 9578 yielded 3422 to 3665 kg ha⁻¹ in replicated trials (Saxena et al. 1983) in Central India. In 1982 ICRISAT and the National Dryland Farming Research Centre, Katumani, Kenya carried out a joint pigeonpea germplasm collection and reported that the Kenyan germplasm is a rich source for drought tolerance and

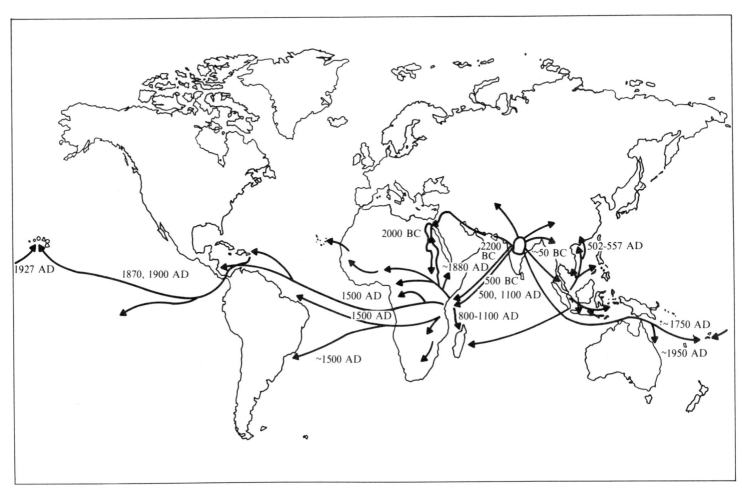

Figure 1. Movement of pigeonpea from its center of diversity.
Source: van der Maesen, 1980.

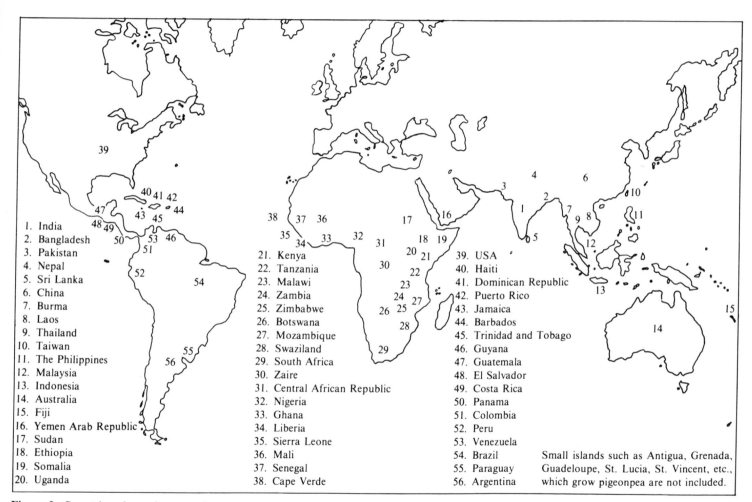

1. India
2. Bangladesh
3. Pakistan
4. Nepal
5. Sri Lanka
6. China
7. Burma
8. Laos
9. Thailand
10. Taiwan
11. The Philippines
12. Malaysia
13. Indonesia
14. Australia
15. Fiji
16. Yemen Arab Republic
17. Sudan
18. Ethiopia
19. Somalia
20. Uganda
21. Kenya
22. Tanzania
23. Malawi
24. Zambia
25. Zimbabwe
26. Botswana
27. Mozambique
28. Swaziland
29. South Africa
30. Zaire
31. Central African Republic
32. Nigeria
33. Ghana
34. Liberia
35. Sierra Leone
36. Mali
37. Senegal
38. Cape Verde
39. USA
40. Haiti
41. Dominican Republic
42. Puerto Rico
43. Jamaica
44. Barbados
45. Trinidad and Tobago
46. Guyana
47. Guatemala
48. El Salvador
49. Costa Rica
50. Panama
51. Colombia
52. Peru
53. Venezuela
54. Brazil
55. Paraguay
56. Argentina

Small islands such as Antigua, Grenada, Guadeloupe, St. Lucia, St. Vincent, etc., which grow pigeonpea are not included.

Figure 2. Countries where pigeonpea is grown.
Source: Sharma et al. (1981)

Table 1. Range of variability in the pigeonpea germplasm.

Character	Minimum	Maximum	Number of observations
50% flowering (days)	55	210	8582
75% maturity (days)	97	260	8561
Plant height (cm)	39	385	8526
Primary branches (number)	2.3	66.0	5812
Secondary branches (number)	0.3	145.3	5793
Racemes (number)	6	915	5812
Seeds per pod	1.6	7.6	8413
100-seed mass (g)	2.8	22.4	8475
Harvest Index (%)	0.6	62.7	5772
Shelling ratio (%)	5.8	86.6	5759
Protein percentage	12.4	29.5	8206

Table 2. Popular pigeonpea cultivars developed by selection from landraces in different states of India.

Cultivars	Origin	Maturity
LRG 30, LRG 36, C 11, ST 1	Local selections from Andhra Pradesh	Medium
BR 183	Local selection from Bihar	Mid-early
BAHAR	Local selection from Bihar	Mid-late
BASANT	Local selection from Bihar	Late
LAXMI	Developed from local selections from Bihar (BR 183 × LOCAL)	Medium
T 15-15	Local selection from Gujarat	Medium
GS 1	Local selection from Karnataka	Medium
PT 221	Local selection from Karnataka	Late
GWALIOR 3	Local selection from Madhya Pradesh	Late
KHARGONE 2	Local selection from Madhya Pradesh	Mid-early
JA 3	Developed from local selections (NO. 148 × GWALIOR 3)	Mid-late
JA 9-19	Local selection from Madhya Pradesh	Medium
AS 71-37	Developed from local collection from Madhya Pradesh	Mid-early
NO. 148	Local selection from Maharashtra	Medium
BDN 1, BDN 2	Local selections from Maharashtra	Medium
CO 1	Local selection from Tamil Nadu	Early
CO 3	A mutant from a local selection (CO 1) from Tamil Nadu	Early
SA 1	Local selection from Tamil Nadu	Medium
CO 4	Selection from a landrace which originated from Andhra Pradesh	Early
TYPE 7, TYPE 17	Local selections from Uttar Pradesh	Late
B 7	Local selection from West Bengal	Late

(Source: Chandra et al. 1983).

high yield (Remanandan et al. 1982). The germplasm was evaluated in Kenya, and 14 selections from these landraces outyielded the best local controls in replicated trials (Shakoor et al. 1984).

Today our pigeonpea collection has grown to 11 034 accessions from 52 countries. The passport information and characterization data are summarized in this catalog in the hope that its availability will enhance the utilization of this germplasm. The data were computerized using a VAX 11/780 computer, and the ICRISAT Data Management and Retrieval System (IDMRS), and analysed by GENSTAT software.

The utility of a collection of this size largely depends upon accessibility to well-defined sections of the collection (Byth 1981). To achieve this objective a number of artificial and natural groups, with frequently required combinations of morphoagronomic traits, have been constituted and presented. The importance of the publication of such information in effective utilization of crop germplasm has been recently emphasized by Hawkes (in press) and Smithson (in press). We will continue to review this classification in response to new developments in crop improvement.

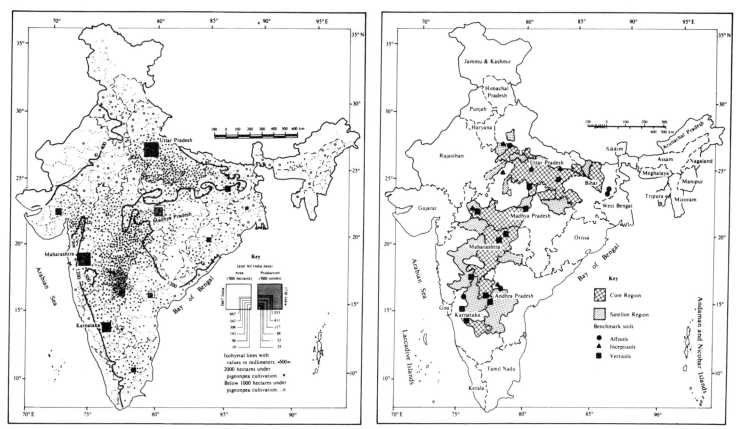

Figure 3. Left, distribution, area and production, right, length of growing season in pigeonpea-growing regions in parts of India.
Source: Huda and Virmani 1987.

The data documented can be broadly classified into passport and characterization data. Depending upon the need of the user, various searches are possible in both passport and characterization data. An example of a set of queries using IDMRS follows:

Command   Select ICP with country of origin Kenya

Answer   There are 316. Do you want to name this collection?

Command   Yes

Answer   Enter name for your collection

Command   KENYA.COL

Command   Select ICP in KENYA.COL with seed shape PEA

Answer   There are 6 records in this collection. Do you want to print these states?

Command   Yes

Answer   ICP 9133, 9136, 9145, 9174, 9181, 9187

Command   Select ICP in KENYA.COL with seed weight >15.0g and seed shape PEA

Answer   There are 2 records in this collection. Do you want to print these states?

Command   Yes

Answer   ICP 9133, 9145.

To determine if any of these possess wilt resistance, the user can check manually by referring to the list of wilt resistant lines, which is not a long one. Also, a printout of these accessions with all or a selected set of morphological traits can easily be extracted. It is possible to get results from a more complex series of queries by using a combination of computer and manual procedures.

The characterization data have been summarized for all traits important in pigeonpea improvement. Lines that possess some of the most wanted combinations of traits are also listed as 'ready made' resources. Various further listings are possible, depending upon demand. Based on the feedback from users, this catalog will be revised as necessary.

Passport Information

These data consist of accession identifiers, information on origin and other data recorded by collectors. Passport information is published in a companion volume.

Source of the germplasm

The initial ICRISAT collection consists of the germplasm collected and assembled by the former Regional Pulse Improvement Project (RPIP), a joint project of USDA, India, and Iran. When RPIP was phased out in 1970, sets of this collection remained at the Indian Agricultural Research Institute (IARI), Regional Station at Rajendranagar, near Hyderabad, and several agricultural universities in India. In 1973/74 this material was sent to ICRISAT from these centers. RPIP had also stored one set at the National Seed Storage Laboratory, Fort Collins, Colorado, USA. This material was sent to Puerto Rico and then to ICRISAT. Many of the accessions in the RPIP collection have died. Data on precise origin are not available for many accessions.

We soon realized that this collection was far from complete. Based on the center of diversity, crop statistics and representation in the collection, priority areas for collection were identified in consultation with national and international pigeonpea scientists and IBPGR. ICRISAT then embarked upon a phase of accelerated germplasm assembly (Table 3). In

Table 3. ICRISAT collection expeditions for pigeonpea and its wild relatives.

Year	Area	No. of samples	Germplasm	Year	Area	No. of samples	Germplasm
1974	Madhya Pradesh, India (2 collections)	134	Pigeonpea	1980	Western Ghats, India, (2 collections)	51	*Atylosia*, Pigeonpea
1975	Madhya Pradesh, India	321	Pigeonpea		Sri Lanka	36	Pigeonpea, *Atylosia*
	Western Ghats, India	3	*Atylosia*		Garhwal and Kumaon Hills,		
	West Bengal, Bihar, India	7	Pigeonpea, *Atylosia*		Uttar Pradesh, India	30	*Atylosia*
1976	Southern Hills, India	15	*Atylosia*, Pigeonpea		Eastern Ghats, India	6	*Atylosia*
	Northern Karnataka, India	107	Pigeonpea		Western Nepal	35	Pigeonpea
	Tirumalai, India	1	*Atylosia*		Thailand	72	Pigeonpea, *Atylosia*
	Orissa, Bihar, India	174	Pigeonpea, *Atylosia*		Burma	13	Pigeonpea
	Kenya	120	Pigeonpea		Punjab, India	8	Pigeonpea, *Atylosia*
	Nilgiri Hills, India	9	*Atylosia*		Zambia	21	Pigeonpea
1977	Tamil Nadu, India	8	Pigeonpea	1981	Philippines	83	Pigeonpea
	Eastern Ghats, Bastar,				Tanzania	234	Pigeonpea
	Madhya Pradesh, India	2	*Atylosia*		Attappadi Hills and Silent		
	Eastern Uttar Pradesh, India	189	Pigeonpea		Valley, Southern India	49	Pigeonpea, *Atylosia*
	Northwest India	19	Pigeonpea, *Atylosia*		Mozambique	16	Pigeonpea
	South India	23	Pigeonpea		Eastern Ghats of		
1978	Assam, India	46	Pigeonpea, *Atylosia*		Andhra Pradesh, India	17	Pigeonpea, *Atylosia*
	Gujarat, India	143	Pigeonpea	1982	Kenya	282	Pigeonpea
	Western Ghats, India	6	*Atylosia*		South Africa	5	Pigeonpea
1979	South Indian Hills	42	*Atylosia*		Zimbabwe	3	Pigeonpea
	Australia	19	*Atylosia*	1983	Orissa, India	229	Pigeonpea
	Bangladesh	32	Pigeonpea		Malawi	230	Pigeonpea
	Eastern Nepal	100	Pigeonpea	1985	Caribbean Islands	222	Pigeonpea
	Hill areas of Maharashtra, Gujarat, and Madhya Pradesh, India	20	*Atylosia*	1986	Caribbean/Central American Region	112	Pigeonpea
	Bundelkhand, India	89	Pigeonpea				
	Malawi	21	Pigeonpea				
	Northeastern Hill States, India	22	Pigeonpea, *Atylosia*				

this work, the early efforts of Drs L.J.G. van der Maesen (currently at the Agricultural University, Wageningen, the Netherlands) and Anishetty N. Murthi (currently at IBPGR, Rome) deserve special mention. The wild species related to *Cajanus*, particularly *Atylosia* and other members of the subtribe *Cajaninae*, also received attention. At present we have 271 accessions of 47 species belonging to 6 genera of *Cajaninae*. They have been evaluated for possible use in pigeonpea improvement and many of them are being utilized. Information on wild taxa are summarized in Table 71.

A large number of scientists and institutions cooperated with ICRISAT to assemble the germplasm and carry out collection in various countries. They include:

Dr Laxman Singh (earlier at All India Coordinated Pulses Improvement Project)
Ms Pankaj Reddy (Indian Agricultural Research Institute, Regional Station, Rajendranagar)
Mr C. Sri Ramloo (Andhra Pradesh Agricultural University)
Late Professor S. Ramanujam (All India Coordinated Pulses Improvement Project)
Dr K.C. Arora (National Bureau of Plant Genetic Resources)
Dr H.K. Jain (formerly at Indian Agricultural Research Institute)
Dr B.R. Murthy (formerly at Indian Agricultural Research Institute)
Dr D. Sharma (formerly at Jawaharlal Nehru Krishi Vishwa Vidyalaya)
Dr W.H. Freeman (formerly at Integrated Cereal Program, USAID, Nepal)
Department of Agriculture, Government of Nepal
Central Agricultural Research Institute, Sri Lanka
Chiangmai University, Thailand
University of the Philippines at Los Baños and IRRI, The Philippines
University of Queensland and Department of Primary Industries, Australia
Mr J.F.M. Onim (earlier at University of Nairobi)
Dr Abdul Shakoor (NDFRC/FAO, Nairobi)

Ministry of Agriculture and Governments of Kenya, Tanzania, and Malawi
Dr J.A. Spence (earlier at Trinidad)
Dr R. Abrams (Puerto Rico)
Dr R.P. Ariyanayagam, University of the West Indies, Trinidad
Caribbean Agricultural Research and Development Institute (CARDI), various Units in West Indies
Ministry of Agriculture, Government of Guyana
Fondo Nacional de Investigaciones Agropecuarias (FONAIAP), Ministry of Agriculture, Government of Venezuela.

Passport descriptors

The passport information is published simultaneously in a separate volume. The descriptors are listed and explained below with their computer codes in parentheses.

1. ICRISAT Pigeonpea Accession Number [ICP]. A unique identifier for each accession is assigned by the ICRISAT gene bank when an accession is registered. The accession number is preceded by the letters ICP. Once assigned, this number will never be reassigned to another accession. When an entry is lost, its assigned number is not reused.

Selections within accessions on the basis of seed color were indicated with a dash: e.g., ICP 1234-2. Many of these were discontinued when they were found to have the same characteristics as the original accessions.

2. Accession Name [NAME]. The accession name is the cultivar name or pedigree or code identifying the cultivar given by the donor or institute that developed the line.

3. Country of Origin [COUNTRY]. This describes the country of origin of the accession, not that of the despatcher (Table 4).

Table 4. Number of accessions in the world collection of pigeonpea at ICRISAT by country, 1 April 1988.

Country	No. of accessions	Country	No. of accessions
Antigua	2	Nigeria	43
Australia[1]	60	Pakistan	14
Bangladesh	73	Peoples' Republic	
Barbados	25	of China	1
Belgium[1]	2	Peru	5
Brazil	16	Puerto Rico	78
Burma	68	Rwanda	5
Cape Verde	6	Senegal	10
Colombia	5	Sierra Leone	3
Dominican Republic	63	South Africa	4
Ethiopia	14	Sri Lanka	71
German Democratic		St. Kitts-Nevis-	
Republic[1]	2	Anguilla	6
Ghana	2	St. Lucia	15
Grenada	15	St. Vincent	22
Guadeloupe	22	Taiwan	3
Guyana	28	Tanzania	221
India	9084	Thailand	17
Indonesia	12	The Philippines	58
Italy[1]	3		
Jamaica	60	Trinidad and	
Kenya	316	Tobago	112
Malagasy Republic	1	Uganda	1
Malawi	245	UK[1]	3
Martinique	1	USA	3
Mexico	2	USSR	2
Montserrat	4	Venezuela	16
Mozambique	10	Zambia	20
Nepal	116	Unknown	10
Total			11 034

1. Secondary source, original source not known.

4. Province of Origin [PROVINCE].

The province of origin of accession is normally the name of the largest administrative sub-division of the country. For example, in India the states are referred to in this descriptor. The origin of the accessions from India are shown in Table 5.

Table 5. Pigeonpea accessions in ICRISAT gene bank from Indian states, 1 April 1988.

State	Number of accessions
Andhra Pradesh	2134
Assam	102
Bihar	669
Daman	1
Gujarat	136
Haryana	12
Himachal Pradesh	4
Karnataka	265
Kerala	47
Madhya Pradesh	624
Maharashtra	628
Meghalaya	2
New Delhi	128
Orissa	322
Punjab	12
Rajasthan	90
Sikkim	4
Tamil Nadu	383
Uttar Pradesh	2121
West Bengal	107
ICRISAT-developed lines	887
Unknown	406
Total	9084

5. Location of Origin [LOCATION]. This is the precise location of origin, village or place/district from which the accession originated. For some, the pedigree name involves the location. However, for most of the assembled germplasm this is not known. This information is available for all the accessions collected by ICRISAT expeditions.

6. Other Designation [OTHER]. This may be the original number assigned by the collector, usually prefixed by initials. It can also be a number given by a donor or institute.

7. Other Collection [OTHERNR]. This refers to any other identification number or name in other collections for the accession (not the collector's number). For breeding materials brief details of pedigree are provided.

Characterization

Introduction

Characterization is the recording of distinctly identifiable characteristics which are heritable. This needs to be distinguished from preliminary evaluation, which is the recording of a limited number of agronomic traits thought to be important in pigeonpea improvement. This catalog presents the result of the characterization of the presently conserved world collection and the preliminary evaluation of a limited number of accessions.

Gene banks would have museum status only if the characteristics and potential of their accessions were not made known. Systematic description of the accessions will eventually lead to classification in small and well-defined sectors that will facilitate enhanced utilization of the germplasm.

The major objectives of characterization are:

1. to describe accessions, establish their diagnostic characteristics and identify duplicates,
2. to classify groups of accessions using sound criteria,
3. to identify accessions with desired agronomic traits and select entries for more precise evaluation,
4. to develop interrelationships between, or among, traits and between geographic groups of cultivars (Chang 1976), and
5. to estimate the extent of variation in the collection.

To accomplish these objectives a multi-disciplinary approach is essential. At ICRISAT we follow this, and the data generated in various disciplines are fed back to the germplasm data base (Fig. 4).

The major exercise of characterization is carried out at ICRISAT Center, Patancheru, Andhra Pradesh, India (latitude 18°N). Sowing dates, climatological details, and description of soil type are given in the following pages (Tables 6–10 and Figs. 3 and 5). The location is ideal for characterizing medium-maturing genotypes. However, early and late lines do not express their full potential at this location. Therefore, in addition to ICRISAT Center, early maturing lines are evaluated at Hisar, India (latitude 29°N) and late-maturing lines at Gwalior, India (latitude 26°N).

At ICRISAT Center characterization is carried out in Vertisols (black soils). The Vertisols of ICRISAT fields are classified as fine montmorillonitic, isohyperthermic, typic, pellustert (Swindale 1982). The soil profile at a depth of 25-70 cm is as follows: sand 22%, silt 19.1%, clay 57.4%, organic content 0.96%, and pH 8.1. Volumetric water content at field capacity is 0.40 m^3 m^{-3} and the wilting point is 0.27 m^3 m^{-3} (Swindale 1982).

Pigeonpea is usually grown after sorghum and the fields are marginally deficient in nitrogen. Soil tests are carried out prior to sowing, and to ensure satisfactory fertility, a minimal dose of nitrogen and phosphate is applied if needed.

Characterization is done in precision fields by spaced planting under adequate cultural conditions and insecticide protection. Seeds are sown by hand in holes spaced 50 cm apart on ridges, 75 cm apart. Several seeds are sown per hole and the stand is reduced to one plant per hole by thinning. Check cultivars of matching maturity are grown at regular

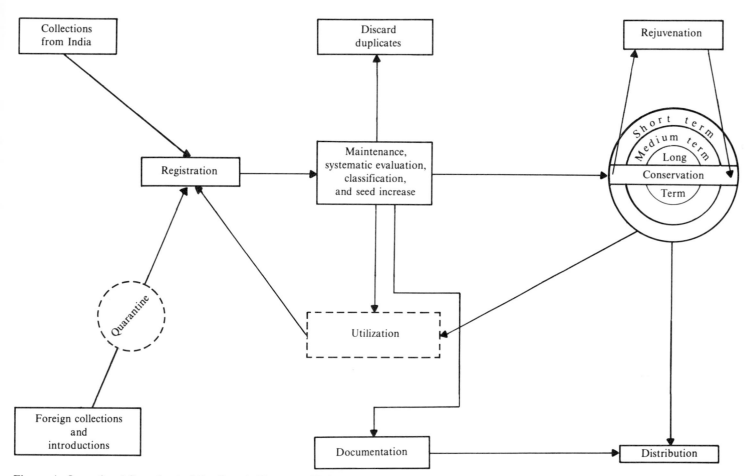

Figure 4. Operational flow chart of the Genetic Resources Unit, ICRISAT.

11

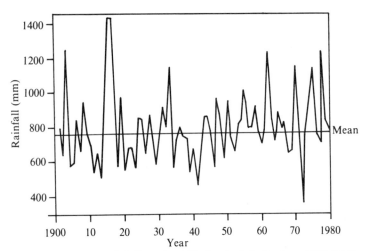

Figure 5. Annual rainfall totals at Hyderabad, India from 1901-1980.
Source: Virmani et al. (1980), and El-Swaify et al. (1985).

Table 6. Sowing dates of pigeonpea germplasm and rainfall at ICRISAT Center, 1975-1986.

Season	Sowing dates	Rainfall after sowing (mm) June-March
1974/75	15 Jun-1 Jul 74	896
1975/76	7 Jul-10 Jul 75	1053
1977/78	16 Jun 77	591
1978/79	26 Jun 78	948
1979/80	26-27 Jun 79	671
1980/81	26 Jun 80	828
1981/82	24 Jun 81	1073
1982/83	17 Jun 82	679
1983/84	15-16 Jun 83	1066
1984/85	18 Jun 84	619
1985/86	19 Jun 85	682

Table 7. Average maximum and minimum monthly temperatures (°C) during the pigeonpea growing season, ICRISAT Center, 1974-1986.

	Maximum										
	1974	1975	1977	1978	1979	1980	1981	1982	1983	1984	1985
Jul	32.1	30.4	30.9	28.9	32.5	30.3	31.3	31.2	31.6	29.8	30.5
Aug	29.4	29.3	29.1	27.8	30.0	28.7	28.3	30.0	29.0	29.5	30.0
Sep	29.9	28.9	30.8	29.6	30.3	29.8	29.0	29.7	28.8	30.4	31.1
Oct	28.6	29.0	30.6	30.5	31.2	32.0	29.6	30.3	28.9	30.4	29.4
Nov	28.2	27.1	29.1	29.2	28.8	29.8	28.3	28.5	27.7	28.2	29.0
Dec	27.0	26.6	27.7	27.2	27.8	28.4	26.9	28.2	26.3	29.1	28.3
	1975	1976	1978	1979	1980	1981	1982	1983	1984	1985	1986
Jan	27.8	26.1	28.0	28.5	28.9	27.0	28.5	28.8	28.4	29.0	27.0
Feb	30.9	30.6	29.6	30.1	32.4	32.5	32.0	32.3	29.8	32.9	30.3
Mar	34.5	35.8	34.4	34.6	35.4	33.6	35.0	36.5	34.6	36.8	35.1

	Minimum										
	1974	1975	1977	1978	1979	1980	1981	1982	1983	1984	1985
Jul	22.4	22.2	22.5	22.1	23.1	22.8	23.0	22.6	23.2	22.3	22.2
Aug	21.7	22.0	22.3	21.7	22.1	21.9	21.8	22.5	22.6	21.9	22.4
Sep	21.6	21.5	21.7	21.0	22.1	21.8	22.2	21.9	22.1	21.6	21.9
Oct	20.2	21.2	20.0	20.0	20.6	18.3	19.9	19.8	20.1	19.7	17.9
Nov	13.3	13.9	20.4	18.6	19.4	16.4	15.0	17.3	13.8	13.5	13.4
Dec	10.6	9.8	13.0	15.2	14.9	13.8	13.9	13.2	14.2	13.7	13.4
	1975	1976	1978	1979	1980	1981	1982	1983	1984	1985	1986
Jan	12.5	11.5	15.8	15.9	15.0	14.1	15.6	13.1	16.1	16.5	13.4
Feb	16.8	13.6	18.1	18.7	17.9	15.8	18.4	17.0	17.7	16.4	17.4
Mar	18.7	18.4	·19.8	19.0	20.0	19.8	20.9	19.9	19.2	20.2	20.1

Table 8. Average relative humidity (%) measured at 0717 and 1417 h during the pigeonpea growing season, ICRISAT Center, 1974-1986.

RH (%) at 0717 h											
	1974	1975	1977	1978	1979	1980	1981	1982	1983	1984	1985
Jul	88	89	85	90	82	83	84	85	89	88	89
Aug	88	91	88	89	86	89	89	86	94	85	85
Sep	94	93	84	90	87	87	91	92	94	87	88
Oct	94	94	87	88	84	78	88	89	90	86	87
Nov	88	92	87	86	91	78	82	91	82	80	80
Dec	88	89	81	81	85	78	84	92	89	84	84
	1975	1976	1978	1979	1980	1981	1982	1983	1984	1985	1986
Jan	85	86	83	87	80	81	88	86	90	90	89
Feb	85	76	83	82	74	61	73	75	78	69	88
Mar	69	56	61	59	66	70	69	61	63	58	65

RH (%) at 1417 h											
	1974	1975	1977	1978	1979	1980	1981	1982	1983	1984	1985
Jul	55	67	61	68	62	62	57	58	60	66	59
Aug	63	68	67	70	61	69	70	61	75	60	61
Sep	64	70	53	64	61	62	70	65	70	56	56
Oct	62	67	46	48	46	32	53	50	59	46	50
Nov	38	43	49	49	55	36	40	49	38	33	34
Dec	33	30	31	39	38	36	40	49	38	33	34
	1975	1976	1978	1979	1980	1981	1982	1983	1984	1985	1986
Jan	31	36	36	37	34	38	39	33	43	39	39
Feb	36	23	37	41	33	19	32	27	40	22	37
Mar	26	17	20	21	31	27	27	23	21	19	25

Table 9. Average daily pan evaporation rate (mm) during the pigeonpea growing season, ICRISAT Center, 1974-1986.

Evaporation rate (mm)											
	1974	1975	1977	1978	1979	1980	1981	1982	1983	1984	1985
Jul	7.7	4.6	5.7	4.5	7.6	5.8	6.5	6.9	6.3	5.2	5.9
Aug	5.2	4.3	4.2	3.6	5.8	4.0	4.1	5.8	4.1	5.8	5.4
Sep	4.8	3.6	5.5	4.2	4.2	4.5	3.9	4.6	3.6	5.4	5.4
Oct	3.7	3.9	5.0	5.2	5.3	6.0	4.3	4.8	4.0	5.1	4.9
Nov	4.8	4.3	4.5	4.3	4.1	5.6	4.5	4.4	4.6	5.7	5.5
Dec	4.4	4.7	4.7	4.7	4.4	5.4	4.6	4.8	4.0	4.8	3.6
	1975	1976	1978	1979	1980	1981	1982	1983	1984	1985	1986
Jan	4.8	6.1	4.8	5.3	5.4	5.0	5.4	5.5	4.8	5.5	4.9
Feb	6.1	6.9	6.1	6.1	7.2	8.1	7.1	7.5	6.7	7.5	6.6
Mar	8.4	9.1	10.4	9.4	9.4	9.3	9.2	9.8	8.3	9.4	9.4

Table 10. Average duration (h) of daily bright sunshine during the pigeonpea growing season, ICRISAT 1974-1986.

Sunshine duration (h)											
	1974	1975	1977	1978	1979	1980	1981	1982	1983	1984	1985
Jul	5.6	3.9	4.5	3.3	5.7	3.1	4.4	5.9	4.7	3.5	4.3
Aug	4.4	4.4	3.8	3.0	5.4	4.5	4.0	4.2	3.6	5.5	5.2
Sep	6.4	4.3	7.7	5.6	5.5	5.8	5.2	5.5	3.9	6.3	6.0
Oct	6.2	3.8	8.5	9.0	7.5	9.4	7.4	8.3	6.7	8.4	7.8
Nov	9.9	8.7	6.8	8.2	7.6	8.8	9.0	8.1	9.8	9.2	9.8
Dec	10.2	10.0	10.0	8.8	9.6	8.8	9.2	9.4	8.2	9.5	8.6
	1975	1976	1978	1979	1980	1981	1982	1983	1984	1985	1986
Jan	10.5	8.7	8.8	9.4	9.9	8.8	9.2	10.0	8.7	9.0	9.1
Feb	9.7	10.5	8.6	8.8	10.3	10.7	9.9	10.1	8.9	10.4	9.9
Mar	8.7	9.3	9.6	9.4	9.4	9.6	10.1	10.3	8.8	9.1	10.2

intervals for comparison. Usually, each accession is grown on 3 ridges 4 m long. Three plants randomly chosen from the middle row are left unbagged and used for recording mostly quantitative traits. The other plants serve for seed increase which is carried out together with characterization. As pigeonpea is a partially cross-pollinated crop, seed increase of accessions must preclude cross-pollination. About 25 plants are covered individually with muslin bags, and the selfed seed from within these bags is bulked to reconstitute the original population. We attempt to increase the seed stock sufficiently in as few cycles as possible to minimize change in the genetic constitution of the accessions.

For each accession 40 morphoagronomic traits are recorded, of which 22 are entered in the computer-based catalog (Table 11). The characterization data are recorded from unreplicated plots which are subject to a variety of environmental factors. Therefore, the quantitative traits, particularly yield, harvest index, shelling ratio, etc., are no more than rough indicators of the genetic potential. However, such data will be generally useful particularly if they are compared with the nearest control of similar maturity.

For measuring descriptors 3, 4, 5, 6, 7, 11, 13, 15, 16, and 17, which are mostly qualitative traits, the whole plot is considered, while the traits 1, 2, 8, 9, 10, 12, 14, 18, 19, 20, 21, and 22 are recorded from three randomly chosen plants.

In addition to these we also record the following descriptors. These, being of less immediate utility, are not yet entered in the computer based catalog.

Vigor at 50% flowering	Stem thickness
Days to flower initiation	Pod length
Duration of flowering	Pod form
Leaf color	Pod texture
Leaf size	Seed second color
Leaf shape (Fig. 6)	Seed eye color
Leaf texture	Eye color width
Number of tertiary branches	Presence of hilum
Raceme length	Plant stand

Figure 6. Diversity in leaf size and shape; left to right largest, normal, ovate, retuse, sesamum type, and minute.

The germplasm is also systematically screened for photoperiod insensitivity. This descriptor is not entered in the catalog as the major portion of the germplasm is highly sensitive. We are in the process of identifying and purifying lines which are comparatively insensitive and details of these will be published later. Similarly, systematic screening is carried out by other disciplines to identify sources resistant to pests and diseases. Important sources, so far identified, are listed separately.

Characterization descriptors and descriptor states

1. Days to 50% Flowering [FLOW50%]. This refers to days from effective date of sowing to when 50% of plants in the whole plot has at least one open flower. This has a direct bearing on the duration to

Table 11. Characterization descriptors and descriptor states used in this catalog.

S.No.	Descriptor	Descriptor states	S.No.	Descriptor	Descriptor states
1	Days to 50% flowering [FLOW50%]	No. of days	12	Number of racemes [RACEMNR]	Count in numbers
2	Days to 75% maturity [MATURITY]	No. of days	13	Pod color [PDBASCOL]	DP = Dark purple G = Green M = Mixed, green and purple P = Purple
3	Base flower color [BASFLCOL]	I = Ivory LY = Light yellow OY = Orange yellow Y = Yellow	14	Number of seeds per pod [SEEDNR]	Count in numbers
4	Second flower color [SECFLCOL]	NO = None Pu = Purple R = Red	15	Seed color pattern (Fig. 9) [SEEDPATT]	M = Mottled MS = Mottled and speckled P = Plain R = Ringed S = Speckled
5	Pattern of streaks (Fig. 9) [STRKPATT]	DS = Dense streaks FS = Few streaks MS = Medium amount of streaks NO = None P = Plain, uniform coverage	16	Base color of seed [SBASCOL]	B = Brown BL = Black C = Cream DB = Dark brown DG = Dark grey DP = Dark purple G = Grey LB = Light brown LC = Light cream LG = Light grey O = Orange P = Purple RB = Reddish brown W = White
6	Flowering pattern [FLOWPATT]	DT- = Determinate NDT = Indeterminate SDT = Semi-determinate			
7	Growth habit [GROWHAB]	C = Compact S = Spreading SS = Semi-spreading			
8	Plant height at maturity [PLHTMAT]	Measurement in cm			
9	Number of primary branches [NRPRBR]	Count in numbers	17	Seed shape (Fig. 9) [SEEDSHPE]	E = Elongate O = Oval P = Pea S = Square
10	Number of secondary branches [NRSECBR]	Count in numbers			
11	Stem color [STEMCOL]	D = Dark purple G = Green P = Purple R = Sun red	18	Seed mass [SEEDWT]	100-seed mass (g)

Continued.

Table 11. *Continued.*

S.No.	Descriptor	Descriptor states
19	Harvest Index [HI]	Ratio of grain yield to biological yield (%)
20	Shelling ratio [SHRAT]	Dry seed - pod ratio (%)
21	Protein percentage [PROTEIN]	Proportion of protein in whole seed (%)
22	Yield per plant [YLDPERPT]	Grain yield (g)

maturity of the cultivar. A wide range of duration exists in pigeonpea. Duration to maturity is very important in the adaptation of cultivars to various agroclimatic areas and cropping systems. Pigeonpea breeders at ICRISAT have developed a scale of maturity classes with reference cultivars for each maturity. They are presented in Table 12.

Table 12. Maturity classification of pigeonpea when sown at the beginning of the rainy season, ICRISAT Center, 1977-78.

Maturity group	Days to 50% flowering	Reference cultivars
0	<60	PANT A 3
I	61- 70	PRABHAT, PANT A 2
II	71- 80	UPAS 120, BAIGANI
III	81- 90	PUSA AGETI, T 21
IV	91-100	ICP 6
V	101-110	NO. 148, BDN 1
VI	111-130	ICP 1, ICP 6997, ST 1, C 11
VII	131-140	HY 3C, ICP 7035
VIII	141-160	ICP 7065, ICP 7086
IX	>160	NP(WR) 15, GWALIOR 3, NP 69

Source: ICRISAT, Annual Report 1978

This scale is used to classify the pigeonpea germplasm in this catalog. The classification is based on days to 50% flowering at ICRISAT Center, when sown in late June. However, this classification may vary at other locations and seasons. Pigeonpea is a quantitative short-day plant with a critical daylength of 13 h (Sharma et al. 1981) and the duration of genotypes within a class vary in their duration depending on the sowing date, latitude, and altitude as well as the climatic and other environmental conditions of a given location (Sharma et al. 1981). The data are summarized in Figure 7 and Tables 13 and 14.

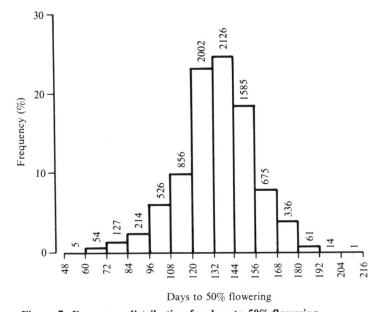

Days to 50% flowering

Figure 7. Frequency distribution for days to 50% flowering.
(In all histograms, figures at top of the bar indicate number of accessions in that class interval)

Table 13. Maturity classification of the pigeonpea world collection sown in June, ICRISAT Center, 1974-1985.

Maturity group	No. of accessions	Frequency (%)
0	5	0.06
I	42	0.49
II	84	0.98
III	162	1.89
IV	215	2.50
V	584	6.80
VI	2306	26.87
VII	1839	21.43
VIII	2584	30.11
IX	761	8.88
Total	8582	

Table 14. Summary of statistics on days to 50% flowering of pigeonpea germplasm, ICRISAT Center, 1974-1985.

Mean	134.4	SD	21.12	CV (%)	15.7
Min.	55	Max.	210	Range	155
Kurtosis	0.61	Skewness	-0.34		
No. of observations	8582				

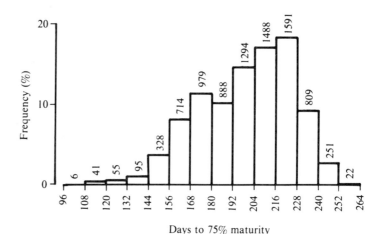

Figure 8. Frequency distribution for days to 75% maturity.

Table 15. Summary of statistics on maturity.

Mean	199.8	SD	26.76	CV (%)	13.4
Min.	97	Max.	260	Range	163
Kurtosis	0.02	Skewness	-0.51		
No. of observations	8561				

2. Days to 75% Maturity [MATURITY]. This refers to number of days taken by 75% of plants in the plot to reach maturity. A plant is considered to have reached maturity when about 75% of its pods are dry.

Though these data (Fig. 8 and Table 15) are recorded for classification of accessions, we use days to flowering more for this purpose, because days to maturity is highly influenced by environmental factors such as soil moisture and temperature. It is also a difficult character to determine accurately.

3. Base Flower Color [BASFLCOL]. The main color of petals is recorded from the whole plot (Plate 1 and Table 16).

4. Second Flower Color [SECFLCOL]. This refers to color of the streaks on the dorsal side of the vexillum (flag) and the second color of the wings and keel (Table 17).

Pattern of streaks

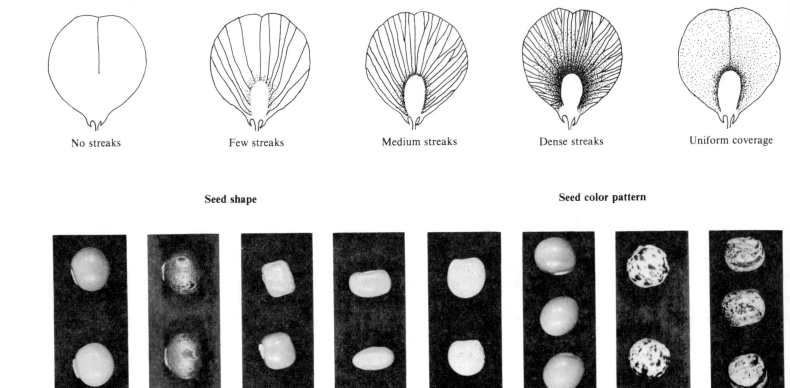

No streaks   Few streaks   Medium streaks   Dense streaks   Uniform coverage

Seed shape   **Seed color pattern**

Oval   Pea   Square   Elongate   Mottled   Speckled   Mottled and speckled   Ringed

Figure 9. Pattern of streaks on flag, seed shape, and seed color pattern.

Plate 1.

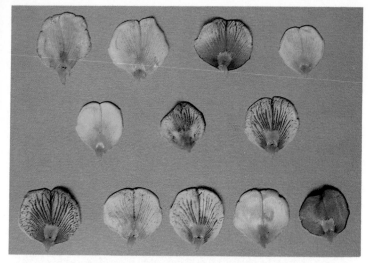

Plate 3.

Plate 2.

Plate 1. Flower classification
Row 1. Base flower color: ivory, light yellow, orange yellow, and yellow.
Row 2. Second flower color: none, purple, and red.
Row 3. Pattern of streaks: dense streaks, few streaks, medium amount of streaks, none, and plain (uniform coverage).

Plate 2. Flowering pattern, left to right; indeterminate, semideterminate, determinate.

Plate 3. Stem classification, top to bottom: dark purple, purple, sun red, and green.

Plate 4.

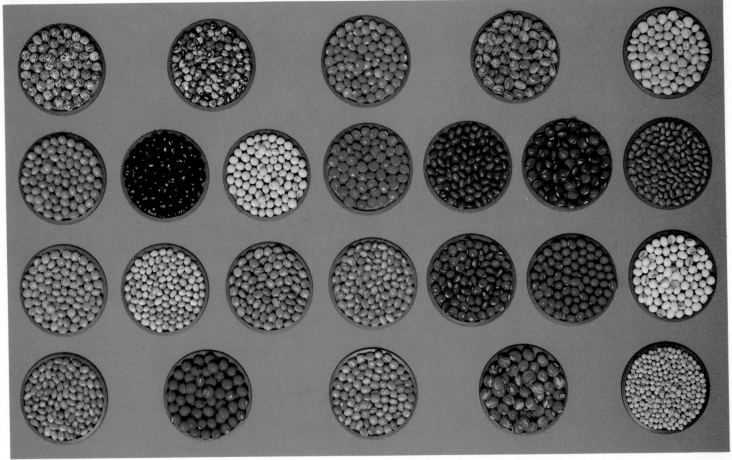

Plate 4. Seed classification
  Row 1. Seed color pattern: mottled, mottled and speckled, plain, ringed, and speckled.
  Rows 2,3. Base seed color: brown, black, cream, dark brown, dark gray, dark purple, gray, light brown, light cream, light gray, orange, purple, reddish brown, and white.
  Row 4. Seed shape and size: elongate, pea, and square (for oval shape refer row 2, brown), largest and smallest.

Plate 5.

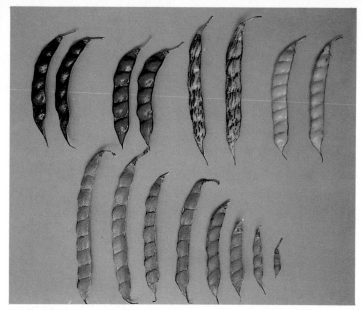

Plate 7.

Plate 6.

Plate 5. Diversity in pod color and size: dark purple, purple, mixed (green and purple), and green, pods with 9 to 2 seeds.

Plate 6. Variation in plant height.

Plate 7. A simple leaf mutant.

Plate 8.

Plate 10.

Plate 9.

Plate 8. Determinate genotype with impressive bunches of pods.

Plate 9. A short statured landrace with several impressive agronomic traits.

Plate 10. *Atylosia volubilis* a wild relative of pigeonpea.

Table 16. Distribution of base flower color.

Code	Flower color	Number of accessions	Frequency (%)
I	Ivory	28	0.32
LY	Light yellow	176	2.05
OY	Orange yellow	69	0.80
Y	Yellow	8287	96.81

Table 17. Distribution of flower color.

Code	Color of streaks	Number of accessions	Frequency (%)
NO	None	490	5.72
PU	Purple	157	1.83
R	Red	7905	92.43

Table 18. Summary of observations on pattern of streaks in pigeonpea flower.

Code[1]	Number of accessions	Frequency (%)
DS	839	9.83
DS+FS	10	0.11
DS+MS	32	0.37
FS	4279	50.17
FS+DS	25	0.29
FS+MS	66	0.77
MS	2564	30.06
MS+DS	63	0.73
MS+FS	25	0.29
NO	490	5.74
P	124	1.45
DS+P	8	0.09
MS+P	1	0.01
P+DS	2	0.02

1. DS = Dense streaks   NO = None
   FS = Few streaks   P = Plain, uniform coverage
   MS = Medium amount of streaks.

5. Pattern of Streaks [STRKPATT]. Figure 9 and Plate 1 illustrate the different descriptor states. Five states are recognized. Combinations of different states occur in some accessions (Table 18).

6. Flowering Pattern [FLOWPATT]. The pattern of flowering habit is recorded from the whole plot (Plate 2 and Table 19).

Most traditionally grown pigeonpeas have indeterminate flowering habit (Table 19). The inflorescences develop as axillary racemes from all over the branches and flowering proceeds acropetally from base to apex both within the racemes and on the branches. The flowering period is often prolonged enabling the plant to recover from various stresses to which the pigeonpea plant is exposed. Some genotypes are morphologi-

Table 19. Distribution of pigeonpea flowering pattern.

Code	Flowering pattern	Number of accessions	Frequency (%)
DT	Determinate	298	3.47
NDT	Indeterminate	8186	95.38
SDT	Semi-determinate	94	1.09

cally determinate (Table 20). In these types the apical buds of the main shoots develop into inflorescences. Here the sequence of inflorescence production is basipetal. There are genotypes intermediate between these two types, which are referred to as semi-determinate. Here the flowering starts at nodes behind the apex and proceeds both acropetally and basipetally. Plate 2 illustrates these three descriptor states.

Most of the determinate genotypes are genetically advanced, and are products of breeding programs. They are generally short in stature and bear clusters of pods at the top of the plant canopy more or less at the same height, maturing at the same time (Plate 8). Hence, they are easier to spray and harvest mechanically. However, they are prone to heavy insect attack and therefore have a definite disadvantage when they are not heavily protected by insecticides (ICRISAT 1976). The determinate habit confers no advantage in yield or in the partitioning of dry matter into seeds (ICRISAT 1979).

Table 20. Maturity classification of determinate (DT) and semi-determinate (SDT) pigeonpea accessions.

Maturity group	Number of accessions	
	DT	SDT
0	2	0
I	36	0
II	33	3
III	45	1
IV	31	2
V	41	3
VI	65	12
VII	19	18
VIII	23	41
IX	3	14
Total	298	94

ICP numbers of accessions with determinate flowering pattern

Group 0

1153	11737					

Group I

6974	10898	10899	10903	10904	10905	10906
10907	10908	10909	10910	10911	10913	10914
10915	10916	10917	10918	10919	10920	10921
10922	10923	10924	10925	10926	10927	10928
10929	11628	11633	11634	11637	11718	11739
11765						

Group II

7642	10900	10901	10902	11504	11539	11542
11546	11548	11549	11550	11595	11598	11599
11600	11605	11607	11609	11610	11612	11621
11622	11623	11625	11626	11627	11629	11630
11631	11632	11638	11655	11662		

Group III

28	3861	7123	7126	7130	7131	7135
7138	7139	7140	7142	7143	7144	7145
7146	7147	7148	7150	7164	7165	7170
7220	7533	7631	7763	7764	11502	11543
11547	11594	11602	11606	11608	11619	11620
11624	11636	11647	11648	11653	11656	11657
11658	11659	11660				

Group IV

4	3868	3789	7124	7125	7127	7128
7129	7132	7141	7151	7163	7166	7167
7169	7171	7172	7173	7174	7269	8805
9126	9127	11500	11501	11505	11511	11523
11561	11635	11654				

Continued

ICP numbers of accessions with determinate flowering pattern

Group V

6917	6932	6943	7121	7122	7133	7134
7136	7137	7149	7152	7153	7154	7155
7157	7158	7159	7160	7161	7162	7168
7637	11112	11136	11277	11478	11480	11522
11527	11529	11564	11565	11568	11570	11572
11573	11575	11579	11585	11664	11666	

Group VI

3756	6523	6524	6525	6615	6909	6914
6915	6916	6930	7050	7057	7205	7208
7210	7211	7214	7215	7263	7284	7609
8557	8559	9878	10082	10086	10102	10118
11108	11479	11506	11508	11509	11510	11512
11515	11516	11517	11518	11519	11520	11521
11528	11530	11536	11558	11559	11563	11567
11569	11571	11574	11576	11577	11578	11580
11581	11583	11584	11611	11663	11665	11667
11669	11976					

Group VII

6516	6518	6919	6920	6924	7209	7212
7283	8148	8561	10080	10172	10175	10176
10299	11668	11670	11853	11863		

Group VIII

6060	6200	6366	6857	6907	6908	6912
6936	7213	7282	7285	8000	8675	8678
10733	11103	11769	11773	11775	11849	11850
11856	11862					

Group IX

6840	7197	11176

ICP numbers of accessions with semi-determinate flowering pattern

Group II

7028	7655	8387

Group III

7652

Group IV

7653	9045

Group V

7650	7668	8715

Group VI

1889	3755	6841	7342	7407	8338	8945
8955	8956	8958	8997	9331		

Group VII

1684	2083	4304	4311	4318	4659	5470
6369	6519	6750	7115	7201	7845	8514
8533	8547	8854	11145			

Group VIII

4264	4289	4291	4305	4316	4330	4331
4699	4741	5914	6392	6527	6623	6673
6693	6697	6713	6748	6794	6896	6906
6925	7035	7187	7264	7266	7336	7337
7403	7436	7452	8051	8545	8708	9877
11143	11165	11191	11481	11990	12190	

Group IX

6781	6798	6891	7194	7196	7259	7267
7286	7372	7532	8687	8688	8693	11905

7. Growth Habit [GROWHAB]. This refers to the pattern of growth and plant habit, recorded from the whole plot.

Pigeonpea cultivars differ markedly in growth habit and plant canopy. The growth habit depends mainly upon the number of primary and secondary branches and the angle of branches on the stem on which they are borne resulting in a continuous variety of forms, from upright compact to spreading types. The plant habit is an important factor which influences the optimum plant population, which varies from 6000 to over 300 000 plants ha^{-1} (Abrams and Julia 1973; Ariyanayagam 1975; Saxena and Yadav 1975). This character is also of critical importance in various intercrop situations.

For this trait pigeonpea accessions are classified into three categories (Table 21):

Compact (C)　　Having relatively few branches, which are borne at narrow angles to the stem, resulting in a compact plant habit.

Spreading (S)　　Having relatively many branches, resulting in a broad plant canopy. Such types (Table 22) are often preferred in some intercrop situations where they will cover the area vacated by a companion crop. However, they often do not make optimum use of solar radiation.

Semi-spreading (SS)　　Being intermediate between the above two types, most genotypes belong to this group.

Since landraces are not pure lines, there are often variations amongst individual plants in an accession. For example, some accessions have both compact and semi-spreading plants.

8. Plant Height at Maturity [PLHTMAT]. Three randomly chosen plants are measured in centimeters at the time of maturity, and the average height is recorded.

Table 21. Distribution of growth habit.

Code[1]	No. of accessions	Frequency (%)
C	1005	11.71
C+SS	10	0.11
S	233	2.71
S+SS	1	0.01
SS	7313	85.23
SS+C	18	0.20

1. C = Compact, S = Spreading, SS = Semi-spreading.

Table 22. Maturity classification of pigeonpea accessions with spreading growth habit.

Maturity group[1]	No. of accessions
0-II	0
III	1
IV	4
V	28
VI	87
VII	42
VIII	47
IX	24
Total	233

1. See Table 12 for maturity scale.

This trait is related to maturity, photoperiod sensitivity, and environment and has low heritability (Sharma 1981). Long-duration pigeonpeas are generally tall because of their prolonged vegetative phase. However, their height will be substantially reduced when they are forced to flower early by photoinduction. Similarly, short-duration pigeonpeas are comparatively short in stature because their vegetative growth phase is short.

ICP numbers of accessions with spreading growth habit

Group III

13						

Group IV

352	1184	7405	7449

Group V

18	355	359	369	444	512	1105
2732	2755	2900	3795	7415	7416	7418
7419	7429	7437	7440	7443	7444	7446
7447	7600	7756	7758	8046	9808	9810

Group VI

126	363	424	440	496	744	806
1063	1090	1613	1854	1857	2619	2812
2849	2939	3327	3990	6484	6485	6488
6492	6494	6499	6502	6503	6705	7050
7057	7228	7304	7338	7347	7348	7383
7392	7393	7397	7399	7400	7401	7402
7404	7412	7441	7450	7465	7616	7666
7675	7713	7743	7744	7748	7898	7931
7932	7933	7934	7935	7936	7938	7951
7971	8021	8875	8878	8880	9238	9681
9773	9775	9789	9800	9801	9802	9805
9806	9807	9809	9812	9814	9815	9816
9820	9821	9822				

Group VII

388	865	2290	2696	3430	3521	3561
3575	4142	5133	6700	6714	6978	7245
7247	7305	7745	7747	7881	7937	7939
7946	7947	7950	7952	7953	7960	7961
7963	8215	8384	8385	8393	8561	8877
8883	9007	9267	9680	9798	9813	11971

Continued

ICP numbers of accessions with spreading growth habit

Group VIII

962	967	1658	1959	3534	3739	3904
3997	4168	4935	5424	5560	5799	5802
5957	5971	6491	6573	7040	7045	7047
7289	7531	7558	7561	7565	7568	7570
7573	7578	7587	7590	7596	7615	7940
7941	7945	7949	7954	7955	7956	7962
8211	8389	8635	8637	8657		

Group IX

3930	7204	7221	7332	7365	7475	7478
7482	7486	7498	7499	7500	7504	7505
7509	7510	7513	7514	7536	7553	7554
7588	7591	7595				

Their height can be substantially increased through prolongation of the vegetative phase by exposure to long day conditions. Thus, this character varies according to location and time of sowing. But there are genetic dwarfs (Plate 6) which will remain as dwarfs in a wide range of environments. The classification presented here is based on measurements taken in June/July sowing at ICRISAT Center (Fig. 10 and Tables 23 and 24).

9. Number of Primary Branches [NRPRBR]. This refers to the average number of branches borne on the main stem per plant recorded from three plants at the time of harvest. This trait is highly heritable (Govinda Raju and Sharat Chandra 1972) and has a high positive correlation with yield (Beohar and Nigam 1972). The data are summarized in Figure 11 and Table 25.

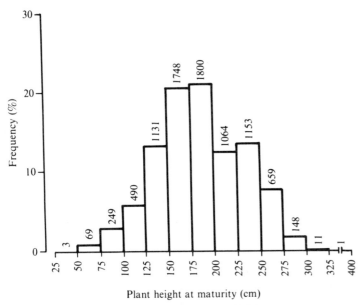

Figure 10. Frequency distribution for plant height.

Table 24. Distribution of germplasm by plant height (cm).

Plant height (cm)	No. of accessions
<50	3
50-100	318
100-150	1621
>150	6584

Table 23. Summary of statistics on plant height (cm).

Mean	187.4	SD	47.38	CV (%)	25.2
Min.	39	Max.	385	Range	346
Kurtosis	-0.376	Skewness	0.003		
No. of observations	8526				

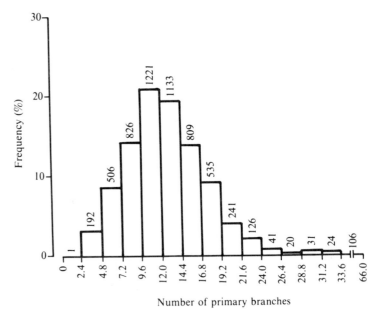

Figure 11. Frequency distribution for primary branches per plant.

Table 25. Summary of statistics on number of primary branches.

Mean	13.2	SD	6.24	CV (%)	47.2
Min.	2.3	Max.	66.0	Range	63.7
Kurtosis	10.03	Skewness	2.24		
No. of observations	5812				

Table 26. Summary of statistics on number of secondary branches.

Mean	31.8	SD	16.57	CV (%)	51.9
Min.	0.3	Max.	145.3	Range	145.0
Kurtosis	0.03	Skewness	0.80		
No. of observations	5793				

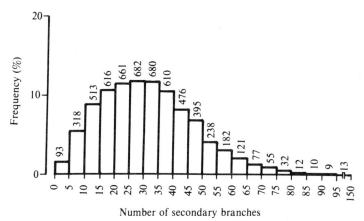

Figure 12. Frequency distribution for secondary branches per plant.

10. Number of Secondary Branches [NRSECBR]. These data, (Fig. 12 and Tables 26 and 27) are also recorded at the time of harvest and they refer to the total number of branches borne on all the primary branches. The average of three plants is taken. More secondary branches occur on the primary branch in plants with a spreading habit. High plant spread is regarded as an effective attribute of grain yield (Dasappa and Mahadevappa 1970).

In all cultivars branching is greatly reduced in dense plantings and in intercropping systems where they are shaded by companion crops (Sheldrake 1984).

11. Stem Color [STEMCOL]. Color of stem is recorded at the time of 50% flowering from all plants in the plot. The most common color is green (Table 28). Other colors are dark purple, purple, and sun red (Plate 3). Purple stem color is dominant to green (D'Cruz and Deokar 1970) and the inheritance follows a simple Mendelian ratio. This purple stem color is useful as marker gene, and we have many purified lines that incorporate this trait (Table 29).

Table 27. Maturity classification of profusely branching accessions (with >50 secondary branches).

Maturity group[1]	No. of accessions
0-III	0
IV	1
V	30
VI	286
VII	151
VIII	220
IX	61
Total	749

1. See Table 12 for maturity scale.

Table 28. Distribution of stem color.

Code[1]	No. of accessions	Frequency (%)
D	1	0.01
G	5058	59.04
G+P	5	0.05
G+R	3	0.03
P	165	1.92
P+G	2	0.02
P+R	1	0.01
R	3325	38.81
R+G	7	0.08

1. D = Dark purple, G = Green, P = Purple, R = Sun red.

Table 29. Maturity classification of accessions with purple stem color.

Maturity group	No. of accessions
0-I	0
II	1
III	7
IV	5
V	2
VI	26
VII	24
VIII	55
IX	45
Total	165

ICP numbers of accessions with purple stem color

Group II

7101						

Group III

3254	6487	7100	7102	7104	7105	7112

Group IV

3722	6400	6565	7113	7567		

Group V

6979	10328					

Group VI

1066	2602	2717	2812	2836	3195	3431
3576	3885	4834	5637	6637	6705	6966
7272	7284	7330	7411	7445	7451	7472
9771	9867	10317	11003	11019		

Group VII

257	1728	2083	4860	5384	5999	6359
6519	6885	7274	8449	8458	8490	9262
9270	9512	10172	10642	10960	11080	11244
11248	11279	11853				

Group VIII

962	2377	3904	3961	4180	4325	4328
4769	4788	4991	5381	5541	5893	5979
6049	6284	6353	6388	6392	6763	7090
7264	7280	7403	7452	7989	8003	8067
8186	8500	9101	9131	9135	9152	9169

Continued

ICP numbers of accessions with purple stem color						
9177	9185	9255	10161	10295	10517	10518
10531	10539	10584	10589	10622	10843	11147
11169	11175	11850	11851	11862	11995	

Group IX

6798	7196	7197	7288	7372	9134	9139
9140	9142	9143	9148	9149	9150	9151
9156	9157	9158	9168	9174	9180	9181
10628	11113	11373	11771	11811	11813	11846
11848	11852	12083	12084	12086	12089	12090
12092	12100	12110	12115	12123	12137	12142
12147	12162	12181				

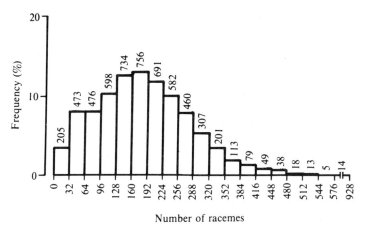

Figure 13. Frequency distribution for number of racemes per plant.

12. Number of Racemes [RACEMNR]. The average number of racemes per plant is recorded from three plants at the time of 50% flowering (Fig. 13 and Tables 30 and 31). Pigeonpea produces very many flowers, of which about 90% are shed without setting pods (Pathak 1970, Ariyanayagam 1975, Sheldrake et al. 1979, Tayo 1980, Pandey and Singh 1981). Therefore, the number of flowers produced cannot be regarded as a major yield component.

Table 31. Maturity classification of accessions with >500 racemes per plant.

Maturity group	No. of accessions
0-IV	0
V	1
VI	13
VII	7
VIII	17
IX	1
Total	39

Table 30. Summary of statistics on raceme number.

Mean	186.0	SD	101.21	CV (%)	54.4
Min.	6	Max.	915	Range	909
Kurtosis	1.67	Skewness	0.8		
No. of observations	5812				

ICP numbers of accessions with >500 racemes per plant						
Group V						
8081						
Group VI						
562	3545	7412	7933	8726	8727	9625
9640	9656	9817	9861	9873	10502	
Group VII						
7946	8456	9484	9520	9691	9757	11947
Group VIII						
4756	4961	7054	7941	7944	8088	8090
8096	8097	8126	8144	8155	8160	8242
8283	8299	8978				
Group IX						
8464						

Table 32. Distribution of pod color.

Code[1]	No. of accessions	Frequency (%)
DP	4	0.04
DP, G	1	0.01
G	476	5.61
G, M	25	0.29
G, PU	1	0.01
M	7673	90.45
M, G	11	0.12
M, PU	20	0.23
PU	249	2.93
PU, G	2	0.02
PU, M	21	0.24

1. DP = Dark purple, M = Mixed, green and purple,
   G = Green, PU = Purple.

Table 33. Maturity classification of accessions with purple pod base color.

Maturity group	No. of accessions
0-II	0
III	2
IV	2
V	7
VI	38
VII	46
VIII	102
IX	52
Total	249

13. Pod Color [PDBASCOL]. The main color of the pods is recorded when the pods are in seed filling stage from all plants in the plot. Based on color, pods are classified as dark purple, purple, mixed (green and purple), and green (Plate 5). Data are summarized in Tables 32 and 33.

ICP numbers of accessions with purple pod base color

Group III

7001	7004					

Group IV

7837	9045					

Group V

3776	6557	7137	7726	7825	8499	10328

Group VI

35	299	990	2144	2560	2828	3431
6512	6523	6524	6525	6841	6996	7214
7215	7226	7256	7263	7378	7453	7804
7900	8059	8098	8193	9612	9614	10082
10088	10342	10383	10713	10864	10875	10933
10936	10939	10940				

Group VII

81	865	969	1923	2562	2682	5599
6518	6547	6550	6551	6578	6612	6661
6666	6719	6721	6737	6740	6742	6884
6899	7209	7212	7251	7258	7855	7992
7994	7998	8116	8178	8370	8414	8428
8433	8449	8482	8514	8546	8777	10703
10876	10886	10999	11248			

Group VIII

663	1220	2286	2786	2923	3782	3923
4168	4404	4796	5468	5529	5541	5625
5804	5838	5979	6038	6132	6520	6521
6549	6691	6697	6699	6722	6724	6728
6734	6735	6739	6741	6770	6773	6808
6809	6812	6829	6848	6854	6888	6893
6894	6906	6908	6933	6970	6975	7032
7034	7035	7038	7058	7213	7216	7236
7255	7257	7278	7337	7621	7870	8029
8104	8107	8110	8111	8122	8127	8139
8539	8543	8544	8545	8596	8601	8619
8639	8649	8696	8847	8853	8861	9689
10081	10096	10103	10235	11040	11105	11175
11178	11262	11263	11276	11380	11412	12002
12019	12068	12153	12159			

Group IX

1998	4135	6729	6798	6890	6897	6898
7196	7206	7227	7286	7512	8677	8687
8688	8860	9021	9026	9028	9029	9030
9031	9032	9047	9048	9052	9158	10880
11038	11160	11322	11336	11353	11359	11369
11370	11373	11375	11376	11378	11382	11388
11392	11398	11449	11804	11915	11916	11930
11988	12066	12161				

Continued

14. Number of Seeds per Pod [SEEDNR]. The number of seeds per pod is determined from 10 pods picked randomly from three plants at harvest time (Fig. 14 and Tables 34 and 35). Although there are large variations between genotypes in seed number per pod, and also in seed size, these are remarkably constant within a given genotype (Sheldrake 1984). The number of seeds per pod is an important component of yield (ICRISAT 1975). In areas where pigeonpea is used as a vegetable, there is a strong consumer preference for cultivars with many seeds per pod (cover photograph).

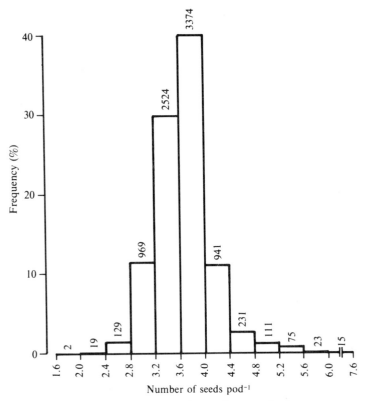

Figure 14. Frequency distribution for seeds per pod.

Table 34. Summary of statistics on seed number per pod.

Mean	3.74	SD	0.48	CV (%)	12.7
Min.	1.6	Max.	7.6	Range	6.0
Kurtosis	4.48	Skewness	0.97		
No. of observations	8413				

Table 35. Maturity classification of accessions with >5 seeds per pod.

Maturity group	No. of accessions
0-IV	0
V	3
VI	21
VII	20
VIII	52
IX	51
Total	147

ICP numbers of accessions with >5.0 seeds per pod

Group V

6917	7719	9799

Group VI

268	281	3099	6523	6915	6930	7210
7211	7353	7898	7901	7916	7921	7925
7926	8535	9607	9624	9639	9811	10875

Group VII

235	3244	7209	7889	7893	7896	7897
7899	7903	7973	7991	8001	8840	8914
9113	9162	9163	9164	9996	11454	

Continued

ICP numbers of accessions with >5.0 seeds per pod

Group VIII

6926	6927	6933	6936	7261	7265	7266
7867	8051	8504	8543	8572	8642	8654
8695	9107	9112	9120	9152	10002	10003
11460	11461	12014	12015	12019	12020	12028
12029	12030	12031	12034	12035	12037	12039
12040	12041	12044	12045	12046	12049	12052
12053	12054	12055	12059	12061	12068	12069
12075	12165	12180				

Group IX

8692	8693	9033	9134	9137	9149	9150
9151	9157	9159	9160	9166	9176	9181
9189	9192	10880	11466	12005	12006	12007
12011	12048	12051	12066	12067	12072	12079
12087	12090	12091	12092	12100	12102	12114
12128	12135	12136	12137	12138	12139	12142
12143	12144	12145	12148	12151	12161	12162
12164	12184					

15. Seed Color Pattern [SEEDPATT]. The color pattern on the seed coat is recorded after the seed of the whole plot has been sun-dried (Table 36). Figure 9 and Plate 4 illustrate the five descriptor states.

16. Base Color of Seed [SBASCOL]. Base color refers to the main color of the seed coat, recorded after the seed of the whole plot has been sun-dried (Tables 37 and 38). Plate 4 illustrates the various seed-coat colors. The seed-coat color does not affect the color of the *dhal* (split decorticated peas). However, there is often a consumer preference for cultivars with light seed-coat color even in areas where pigeonpea is consumed mainly as *dhal*. In areas where the undecorticated dry seeds or green peas are cooked whole, there is strong preference for light-colored seeds.

Table 36. Distribution of seed color pattern.[1]

Code	Seed color pattern	Number of accessions	Frequency (%)
M	Mottled	929	10.92
MS	Mottled and speckled	348	4.09
P	Plain	4762	56.02
R	Ringed	1	0.01
S	Speckled	724	8.51

1. In addition, 1736 accessions, with a frequency of 20.42% had various combinations of seed color patterns.

Table 37. Distribution of seed base color[1].

Code	Seed base color	Number of accessions	Frequency (%)
B	Brown	47	0.55
BL	Black	2	0.02
C	Cream	1422	16.72
DB	Dark brown	152	1.78
DG	Dark grey	9	0.10
DP	Dark purple	54	0.63
G	Grey	113	1.32
LB	Light brown	508	5.97
LC	Light cream	194	2.28
LG	Light grey	17	0.20
O	Orange	4464	52.51
P	Purple	199	2.34
RB	Reddish brown	546	6.42
W	White	109	1.28

1. In addition, 664 accessions, with a frequency of 7.81%, showed various combinations of seed base color.

Table 38. Maturity classification of accessions with light seed coat color.		
Seed color	Maturity group	Number of accessions
White	0-III	0
	IV	1
	V	6
	VI	17
	VII	10
	VIII	54
	IX	21
	Total	109
Cream	0	0
	I	4
	II	27
	III	19
	IV	36
	V	122
	VI	349
	VII	188
	VIII	421
	IX	256
	Total	1422
Light cream	0-III	0
	IV	4
	V	21
	VI	50
	VII	50
	VIII	61
	IX	8
	Total	194

ICP numbers of accessions with white seed base color

Group IV

1187						

Group V

270	359	1951	2049	7063	7700	

Group VI

400	440	445	466	476	551	569
617	625	628	1110	1117	1336	1601
1877	2550	7734				

Group VII

1045	1199	1514	1845	2064	6628	7977
8920	9008	9862				

Group VIII

876	1644	1669	1846	2085	2307	4024
6364	6658	6682	6791	7043	7044	7061
7066	7068	7526	7527	7530	7531	7613
8051	8077	8084	8129	8130	8136	8151
8152	8220	8572	8585	8589	8674	8704
8710	8919	8921	8971	8976	9009	9085
10033	10038	10043	10048	10051	10056	10550
10850	11228	11389	11790	11883		

Group IX

7495	7503	7507	7528	7529	7532	7534
7592	8044	8689	8990	9108	9145	10732
11371	11408	11780	11820	11821	11858	11882

Group IV

352	1131	1211	4869

Group V

157	355	357	457	752	814	1008
1120	1123	1216	1807	2211	2522	3310
3616	3678	3773	4125	4589	4664	6321

Group VI

151	261	264	267	279	281	339
361	377	649	667	753	804	934
990	1088	1090	1136	1169	1458	1577
1630	1680	2003	2084	2282	2325	2327
2362	2930	3027	3130	3169	3224	3268
3344	3357	3359	3431	3641	3718	3788
3810	3848	3882	4885	5754	6105	6261
6494						

Group VII

242	266	648	659	874	896	930
938	1075	1190	1202	1258	1476	1579
1655	1686	1754	1865	2032	2083	2088
2136	2315	2317	2608	2989	3193	3206
3208	3212	3353	3471	3484	3570	3575
3597	4266	4400	4402	4485	4535	5606
5698	6109	6437	6515	6567	6578	6657
6666						

Group VIII

213	214	246	707	813	909	914
951	974	1038	1071	1220	1319	1941

Continued

1959	1979	1997	2017	2324	2599	2613
3048	3066	3069	3382	3725	3896	3914
4227	4236	4278	4290	4306	4307	4358
4360	4368	4379	4380	4540	4665	4699
4933	5011	5358	5424	5569	5887	6289
6422	6473	6498	6540	6665	6685	6696
7569	7570	7571	7572	7573		

Group IX

1967	1998	3941	4698	6238	6300	7492
7496						

17. Seed Shape [SEEDSHPE]. The seed shape is recorded after the seed of the whole plot is sun-dried. Figure 9 illustrates the four seed shape descriptor states. The most common shape is oval (Table 39). Pea-shaped seed is usually found in cultivars with large seeds, but that does not imply that most of the large-seeded cultivars have pea-shaped seeds. The pea-shaped trait is preferred in areas where pigeonpea is used as a green vegetable. This trait is rare in early maturing pigeonpeas (Table 40).

Table 39. Distribution of seed shape[1].

Code	Seed shape	No. of accessions	Frequency (%)
E	Elongate	8	0.09
O	Oval	7795	91.72
P	Pea	164	1.92
S	Square	293	3.44

1. In addition, 238 accessions with a frequency of 2.80% had various combinations of seed shape.

Table 40. Maturity classification of accessions with pea-shaped seeds.

Maturity group	No. of accessions
0-III	0
IV	1
V	3
VI	19
VII	23
VIII	70
IX	48
Total	164

ICP numbers of accessions with pea-shaped seed

Group IV

9837						

Group V

7996	8468	8469

Group VI

893	1842	3701	4691	6986	7338	7353
7407	7480	7874	7995	8108	8192	8255
8483	9027	11559	11569	11708		

Group VII

1843	2546	6628	7895	7896	7974	7980
7991	7992	7993	7994	8002	8008	8056
8064	8072	8073	8546	10108	10642	10814
11145	12160					

Continued

ICP numbers of accessions with pea-shaped seed

Group VIII

1846	3782	6364	7282	7335	7337	7403
7436	7527	7867	7869	7878	7880	7942
7979	7999	8000	8004	8005	8006	8057
8063	8067	8070	8071	8074	8084	8111
8415	8442	8443	8446	8465	8498	8501
8519	8534	8539	8540	8541	8545	8560
8579	8590	8658	8798	8847	8848	8852
8855	8861	8869	9041	9050	9084	9106
9565	9567	9568	10003	10109	10151	10171
11167	11174	11191	11203	12069	12153	12159

Group IX

6863	7372	7503	7507	7592	7593	9013
9019	9020	9028	9029	9030	9031	9032
9033	9037	9038	9040	9042	9043	9044
9048	9049	9083	9108	9133	9136	9145
9174	9181	9187	10878	10888	10889	10890
11028	11113	11119	11168	11172	11176	11196
11281	11476	11811	11826	11934	12083	

18. Seed Mass [SEEDWT]. The mass (weight) of 100 seeds in grams is recorded after the seed is sun-dried, from a random sample taken from the whole plot. Seed mass is an important yield component (ICRISAT 1975). Cultivars vary widely in this character (Plate 4). Unfortunately large-seeded types generally are poor pod setters. Large seeds are preferred by consumers (Gupta et al. 1981) partly because the pericarp percentage reduces with increase in seed size (ICRISAT 1975). For vegetable-type pigeonpeas, large seeds are strongly preferred.

Seedlings from large seeds (up to 16g per 100) are usually larger and often grow faster than seedlings from small seeds. However, there is no significant effect of seed-grading within a genotype on yield (ICRISAT 1976 and 1977). Data are summarized in Figure 15 and Tables 41-45.

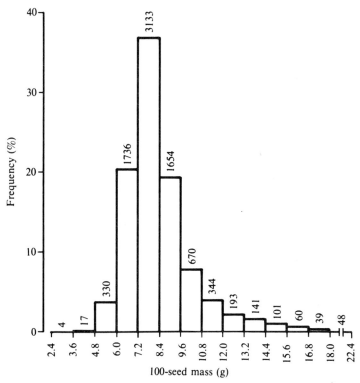

Figure 15. Frequency distribution for 100-seed mass.

Table 41. Summary of statistics on 100-seed mass (g).

Mean	8.54	SD	2.17	CV (%)	25.4
Min.	2.8	Max.	22.4	Range	19.6
Kurtosis	5.96	Skewness	2.02		
No. of observations	8475				

Table 42. Classification of pigeonpea germplasm by 100-seed mass.

100-seed mass (g)	No. of accessions	Frequency (%)
<7	1593	18.79
>7 and <11	6033	71.18
>11 and <15	655	7.72
>15	194	2.28

Table 43. Maturity classification of medium-duration pigeonpea accessions with 100-seed mass >10 g.

Maturity group	No. of accessions
V	82
VI	266
Total	348

Table 44. Maturity classification of pigeonpea accessions with 100-seed mass >15 g.

Maturity group	No. of accessions	Frequency (%)
0-II	0	
III	1	0.51
IV	0	
V	1	0.51
VI	14	7.21
VII	33	17.01
VIII	93	47.93
IX	52	26.80
Total	194	

ICP numbers of accessions with 100-seed mass >15 g

Group III

11653

Group V

9005

Group VI

| 3545 | 6909 | 7215 | 7345 | 7346 | 7367 | 7407 |
| 7480 | 7846 | 11515 | 11528 | 11559 | 11569 | 11576 |

Group VII

3783	3785	6899	6920	7201	7842	7845
7973	7974	7976	7981	7982	7983	7984
7987	7988	7991	8002	8008	8056	8064
8072	8514	8533	8546	8547	8854	10873
10960	11145	11590	11672	12160		

Group VIII

2630	3782	6394	6895	6896	6900	6904
6905	7035	7186	7213	7271	7337	7452
7866	7867	7878	7880	7942	7975	7979
7989	8000	8004	8005	8006	8048	8049
8051	8057	8063	8070	8074	8077	8141
8443	8467	8501	8519	8539	8540	8544
8545	8560	8576	8579	8825	8847	8848
8861	8862	8971	9109	9110	9131	9152
9177	9200	11143	11174	11175	11191	11460
11591	11981	11984	11990	12002	12015	12019
12020	12021	12027	12028	12029	12030	12031
12032	12033	12034	12035	12036	12037	12042
12043	12044	12053	12059	12061	12062	12153
12156	12159					

Continued

ICP numbers of accessions with 100-seed mass >15 g

Group IX

8044	9133	9139	9141	9145	9146	9149
9150	9153	9157	9158	9160	9176	11028
11172	11453	11455	11465	11467	11985	11987
11988	12005	12016	12017	12024	12026	12079
12080	12081	12082	12083	12084	12085	12086
12087	12089	12090	12091	12093	12095	12100
12108	12110	12138	12141	12145	12148	12150
12157	12161	12184				

Table 45. Maturity classification of vegetable-type pigeonpea with 100-seed mass >15 g and >5 seeds per pod.

Maturity group	No. of accessions
0-VI	0
VII	2
VIII	18
IX	16
Total	36

ICP numbers of vegetable-type accessions with 100-seed mass >15 g, and >5 seeds per pod

Group VII

| 7973 | 7991 |

Group VIII

7867	8051	9152	11460	12015	12019	12020
12028	12029	12030	12031	12034	12035	12037
12044	12053	12059	12061			

Group IX

9149	9150	9157	9160	9176	12005	12079
12087	12090	12091	12100	12138	12145	12148
12161	12184					

19. Harvest Index [HI]. The harvest index is the ratio of total grain yield to the total biological yield. Calculations are based on data from three plants obtained in evaluations at ICRISAT Center. The value for total biological yield does not include roots and fallen leaves (Fig. 16 and Tables 46 and 47).

The harvest index of pigeonpeas grown in traditional cropping systems is generally low (Sheldrake 1984). Because it is influenced strongly by environmental conditions, the harvest index is unlikely to be of much value as a selection criterion. It varies markedly under different cropping systems, spacing, growing seasons, and availability of moisture.

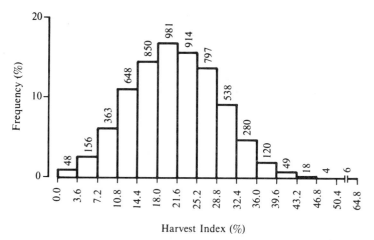

Figure 16. Frequency distribution for Harvest Index.

Table 46. Summary of statistics on Harvest Index (%).

Mean	21.2	SD	8.08	CV (%)	37.9
Min.	0.6	Max.	62.7	Range	62.1
Kurtosis	0.220	Skewness	0.232		
No. of observations	5772				

Table 47. Maturity classification of pigeonpea accessions with Harvest Index >40%.

Maturity group	No. of accessions
0-II	0
III	1
IV	2
V	9
VI	36
VII	14
VIII	6
IX	1
Total	69

ICP numbers of accessions with Harvest Index (HI) >40.

Group III

7220

Group IV

8773	11661

Group V

15	72	8746	9598	10562	10822	11565
11570	11572					

Group VI

569	6841	7348	8724	9206	10707	10747
10748	10751	10752	10753	10754	10759	10765
10767	10768	10784	10794	10795	10821	10827
10830	10866	10870	10930	10934	10935	11506
11507	11577	11682	11683	11684	11685	11698
11707						

Continued

ICP numbers of accessions with Harvest Index (HI) >40.						
Group VII						
9691	10638	10643	10684	10693	10694	10701
10716	10761	10785	10792	10797	10798	10801
Group VIII						
4368	6388	8437	8442	10708	10709	
Group IX						
7579						

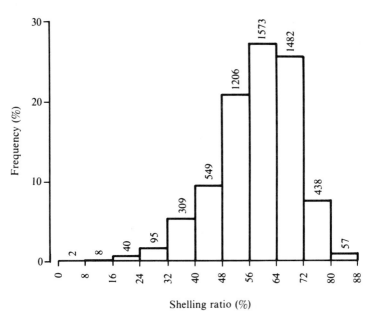

Figure 17. Frequency distribution for shelling ratio.

20. Shelling Ratio [SHRAT]. Shelling ratio refers to the seed:pod ratio, expressed as a percentage based on mass, taken after harvesting and drying. All pods from three plants are used for this record (Fig. 17 and Tables 48 and 49).

Table 48. Summary of statistics on shelling ratio (%).

Mean	58.24	SD	11.67	CV (%)	20.0
Min.	5.8	Max.	86.6	Range	80.8
Kurtosis	0.631	Skewness	-0.653		
No. of observations	5759				

Table 49. Maturity classification of accessions with high shelling ratio (>80%).

Maturity group	No. of accessions	Maturity group	No. of accessions
0-I	0	VI	19
II	1	VII	14
III	3	VIII	6
IV	3	IX	2
V	9		
		Total	57

ICP numbers of accessions with high shelling ratio (>80%)						
Group II						
11662						
Group III						
6958	7630	11647				
Group IV						
7449	7458	8865				
Group V						
359	5856	7387	7446	7856	8332	8348
8746	11703					
Group VI						
255	551	1570	7409	7685	7732	7884
8353	9291	9307	9419	9496	9631	10399
10871	11587	11588	11673	11702		
Group VII						
334	2218	4317	7709	8116	8371	8383
8394	8410	8954	9227	9267	9283	9320
Group VIII						
6655	8267	8619	8980	10978	11963	
Group IX						
7196	9171					

21. Protein Percentage [PROTEIN]. The percentage of protein in mature whole seed is measured by the rapid Technicon Auto Analyser procedure by the ICRISAT Biochemistry Unit. To check the accuracy of this procedure, about every 20th sample is analysed by the standard Micro Kjeldahl (MKJ) procedure. A random sample of seed taken from the whole plot is used.

This analysis has identified many sources of high protein useful in improving the nutritional quality of pigeonpea. However, the richest source of protein (up to 33%) is found in some closely related wild species. This useful trait has already been successfully transferred to the pigeonpea from some *Atylosia* spp and stable lines with high seed protein are now available at ICRISAT (Saxena et al. 1984). Data are summarized in Figure 18 and Tables 50 and 51.

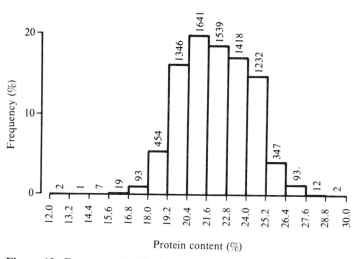

Figure 18. Frequency distribution for protein content.

Table 50. Summary of statistics on protein content (%).

Mean	22.1	SD	2.05	CV (%)	9.2
Min.	12.4	Max.	29.5	Range	17.1
Kurtosis	-0.30	Skewness	0.032		
No. of observations	8206				

Table 51. Maturity classification of high protein accessions (>27%).

Maturity group	No. of accessions
0-I	0
II	3
III	0
IV	0
V	0
VI	5
VII	2
VIII	13
IX	17
Total	40

ICP numbers of accessions with seed protein content >27.0%

Group II

7420	7483	7487				

Group VI

1630	7298	7315	11688	11886		

Group VII

11100	11488					

Group VIII

4213	5529	6799	7069	7257	11276	11470
11472	11766	11794	11840	11883	11970	

Group IX

7291	10967	11110	11182	11183	11223	11225
11227	11282	11309	11316	11431	11709	11796
11814	11817	11879				

22. Yield per Plant [YLDPERPT]. Average grain yield per plant (g) is recorded from three plants in each plot. These yields vary widely, being affected by the environment and so must be compared with the nearest control of the same maturity (Fig. 19 and Table 52).

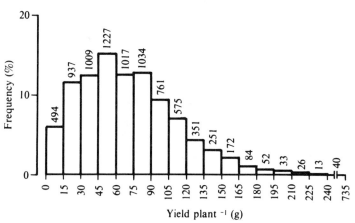

Figure 19. Frequency distribution for grain yield per plant.

Table 52. Summary of statistics on grain yield (g) per plant.

Mean	72.3	SD	46.03	CV (%)	63.6
Min.	1.0	Max.	725.0	Range	724.0
Kurtosis	12.02	Skewness	1.83		
No. of observations	8076				

ICP numbers of accessions with grain yield >300 g per plant

Group VI

5507	5713					

Group VII

1003	1966	2639	9691			

Group VIII

655	780	820	1036	1089	4181	5744
8096	8106	8144	8242	8310		

Correlation Matrix of Characters

A correlation matrix of 12 agronomically important traits is given in Table 53.

The relationship of yield components to seed yield and amongst themselves is a subject of great interest to the plant breeder. The correlation matrix will aid the effective querying of the data base. It will be helpful in the selection of accessions with a desired combination of traits from the collection. When asking for germplasm with a specific trait, users can get some idea of the other traits likely to be associated with the one being considered.

There has been considerable earlier work on this subject using a limited number of genotypes (Singh and Shrivastava 1979, Upadhyaya and Saharia 1980, Dahiya 1980, Asawa et al. 1981, Malik et al. 1981a and b, Ahlawat et al. 1981, Kumar and Reddy 1982, Bainiwal et al. 1983, Dumbre et al. 1985, Sidhu et al. 1985; Balyan and Sudhakar 1985). However, this is the first time that a large (8582 accessions) and diverse collection has been subjected to such an analysis. While considering the

Table 53. Correlation matrix of the important agronomic characters on 8582 pigeonpea accessions evaluated from 1975/76 to 1982/83.

	FLOW50%	MATURITY	PLHTMAT	NRPRBR	NRSECBR	RACEMNR	SEEDNR	SEEDWT	HI	SHRAT	PROTEIN
MATURITY[1]	**0.90**[2]										
PLHTMAT	**0.36**	**0.33**									
NRPRBR	-0.11	-0.08	0.26								
NRSECBR	0.11	0.06	**0.33**	**0.45**							
RACEMNR	-0.11	-0.10	**0.31**	**0.42**	**0.68**						
SEEDNR	0.03	-0.02	0.16	-0.11	-0.15	-0.11					
SEEDWT	0.18	0.18	0.14	-0.18	**-0.30**	**-0.36**	**0.35**				
HI	**-0.43**	**-0.47**	-0.29	-0.06	0.00	0.25	0.00	-0.18			
SHRAT	**-0.39**	**-0.46**	0.04	0.16	0.20	**0.32**	0.06	-0.15	**0.67**		
PROTEIN	**0.39**	**0.35**	0.01	-0.23	-0.12	-0.21	-0.15	-0.06	-0.20	-0.26	
YLDPERPT	-0.17	-0.21	0.26	**0.35**	**0.54**	**0.75**	0.06	-0.16	**0.44**	**0.50**	-0.36

1. See Table 11 for descriptor details.
2. Values above ±0.3 are indicated in bold face.

result of this analysis two facts should be borne in mind. Firstly, all the accessions were not evaluated in one season. Secondly, the measurements are from data covering a wide range of values of the characters under study, and thus, its high values may no longer hold under situations with a much narrower range (Gomez and Gomez 1976). However, the results of this analysis are in agreement with most of the earlier work.

The significant value for these correlations at 1% is 0.155 and the extent of correlation may be classified as follows:

Values >0.3	strongly correlated
Values >0.15 <0.3	moderately correlated
Values <0.15	weakly correlated.

1. Days to 50% flowering and maturity are strongly and positively correlated.
2. Plant height at maturity has a strong positive correlation with days to 50% flowering, maturity, number of secondary branches and racemes. Plant height is also moderately positively correlated with number of primary branches. This is because delay in flowering results in increased vegetative growth and the increase in height results in more branches and racemes.
3. Number of primary branches, an important yield component, is strongly correlated with yield and the other yield components such as the number of secondary branches and racemes.
4. However, number of primary branches, secondary branches, and racemes are negatively correlated with seed mass. Seed mass has been reported to show an inconsistent association with seed yield. A positive association has been reported by Wakankar and Yadav (1975) and Dahiya et al. (1978), and negative by Beohar and Nigam (1972), Ganguli and Srivastava (1972), and Kumar and Haque (1973). Therefore, Malik et al. (1981a) recommended use of a larger number of genotypes for such studies to arrive at some definitive conclusion

regarding the role of seed mass in determining seed yield in pigeonpea. The present analysis reveals a moderate negative correlation between seed mass and seed yield, and this negative relationship of seed mass is quite strong with two important yield components, number of secondary branches and racemes. However, seed mass has a strong positive correlation with seed number per pod.

5. Harvest index and shelling ratio which are calculated figures show a strong positive correlation with yield.

6. A disturbing situation which the correlation matrix revealed is the positive and highly significant correlation between seed protein content and days to 50% flowering and maturity, and a strong negative correlation between protein content and seed yield. However, the trend is not consistent when germplasm evaluated in one season

(Table 54) and accessions originating from one area (Table 55) were considered.

7. In conclusion, number of primary branches, secondary branches, and racemes are the prime contributors to seed yield though plant height contributes significantly by increasing all these traits, which themselves are positively correlated.

To test the validity of these relations, we prepared correlation matrices for the germplasm evaluated in one season (Table 54) and accessions originating from one area, Nepal (Table 55). The trend for most of the relationship is the same. However, the relationship of seed protein content with days to 50% flowering, maturity, and seed yield is not consistent.

Table 54. Correlation matrix of the important agronomic characters on 381 pigeonpea accessions evaluated in 1982/83.

	FLOW50%	MATURITY	PLHTMAT	NRPRBR	NRSECBR	RACEMNR	SEEDNR	SEEDWT	HI	SHRAT	PROTEIN
MATURITY[1]	**0.97**[2]										
PLHTMAT	**0.69**	**0.69**									
NRPRBR	-0.03	0.01	0.14								
NRSECBR	-0.06	-0.04	0.22	**0.59**							
RACEMNR	-0.11	-0.10	0.20	**0.43**	**0.77**						
SEEDNR	**0.44**	**0.43**	0.15	**-0.44**	**-0.59**	**-0.52**					
SEEDWT	**0.42**	**0.41**	0.16	**-0.43**	**-0.60**	**-0.60**	**0.68**				
HI	**-0.40**	**-0.42**	**-0.35**	-0.11	-0.03	0.14	-0.07	-0.14			
SHRAT	0.02	0.00	0.19	0.10	0.28	0.29	-0.17	-0.20	**0.51**		
PROTEIN	-0.06	-0.06	0.12	0.22	0.28	0.29	-0.17	-0.20	-0.09	0.08	
YLDPERPT	0.05	0.05	0.28	0.18	**0.34**	**0.36**	-0.32	-0.40	**0.45**	**0.47**	0.14

1. See Table 11 for descriptor details.
2. Values above ±0.3 are indicated in bold face.

Table 55. Correlation matrix of the important agronomic characters on 112 pigeonpea accessions from Nepal evaluated in 1981/82.

	FLOW50%	MATURITY	PLHTMAT	NRPRBR	NRSECBR	RACEMNR	SEEDNR	SEEDWT	HI	SHRAT	PROTEIN
MATURITY[1]	**0.92**[2]										
PLHTMAT	-0.02	0.03									
NRPRBR	-0.12	-0.06	**0.64**								
NRSECBR	-0.14	0.00	**0.73**	**0.61**							
RACEMNR	-0.24	-0.13	**0.60**	**0.53**	**0.78**						
SEEDNR	-0.16	-0.20	0.19	0.19	0.14	0.17					
SEEDWT	-0.15	-0.20	**0.36**	0.26	0.04	-0.02	**0.35**				
HI	**-0.32**	**-0.38**	0.11	0.23	0.18	**0.32**	**0.38**	0.00			
SHRAT	-0.19	-0.19	**0.68**	**0.53**	**0.59**	**0.62**	0.16	0.15	**0.62**		
PROTEIN	0.28	**0.31**	0.12	0.00	0.06	0.05	**-0.37**	**-0.40**	-0.12	0.03	
YLDPERPT	-0.29	-0.26	**0.66**	**0.57**	**0.74**	**0.85**	**0.31**	0.18	**0.56**	**0.73**	-0.10

1. See Table 11 for descriptor details.
2. Values above ±0.3 are indicated in bold face.

Accessions with Resistance to Biotic Stresses

Major diseases

The major diseases of economic importance are:

1. Wilt (*Fusarium udum* Butler)
2. Sterility mosaic (virus?)
3. Phytophthora blight (*Phytophthora drechsleri* f. sp *cajani*)
4. Witches' broom (virus and mycoplasma?)
5. Rust (*Uredo cajani* Syd.)
6. Leaf spot (*Cercospora cajani* Henn.).

The first three are major yield reducers. Wilt is serious in the Indian subcontinent and eastern Africa; sterility mosaic (SM) and phytophthora blight in India; witches' broom and rust in Central America and the Caribbean; and cercospora leaf spot in India and eastern Africa.

As a result of intensive field and laboratory screening and purifications by pathologists, a wide range of sources of resistance against wilt, SM, and phytophthora blight and combined resistance against more than one disease is now available at ICRISAT. However, it is important to realize that different strains of these pathogens may exist and, there is therefore, no guarantee that these accessions will be resistant at every location. Pedigrees and characteristics of disease resistant accessions are given in Pulse Pathology Progress Report no. 16 (obtainable from the Legumes Program, ICRISAT).

Wilt resistant accessions are listed in Table 56.

A complete list of SM-resistant and tolerant accessions is given in Pulse Pathology Progress Report no. 16. Some of the important resistant accessions are listed below.

Table 56. Pigeonpea accessions resistant to wilt (*Fusarium udum*).

ICP number	Pedigree	Origin of parent line		ICP number	Pedigree	Origin of parent line	
8858	ICWR SEL. SHARDA	Andhra Pradesh,	India	12727	ICWR SEL. 1522	Andhra Pradesh,	India
8859	ICWR SEL. NP(WR) 15	New Delhi,	India	12728	ICWR SEL. 1644	Uttar Pradesh,	India
8860	ICWR SEL. 6970	Madhya Pradesh,	India	12729	ICWR SEL. 2812		Nigeria
8861	ICWR SEL. 7035	Madhya Pradesh,	India	12730	ICWR SEL. 5701	Bihar,	India
8862	ICWR SEL. HY 3C	Andhra Pradesh,		12731	ICWR SEL. 7197	New Delhi,	India
8863	ICWR SEL. 15-3-3	Uttar Pradesh,	India	12732	ICWR SEL. 8464	-	India
8864	ICWR SEL. 20-1	-[1]	India	12733	ICWR SEL. 8795	-	India
8865	ICWR EARLY × EARLY PROG.[2]			12734	ICWR SEL. 8798	-	India
8866	ICWR C.NO. 73039 PROG.[2]			12735	ICWR SEL. 9120	-	Nigeria
8867	ICWR SEL. JA 275	Madhya Pradesh,	India	12736	ICWR SEL. 9144	Machakos,	Kenya
8868	ICWR SEL. 5174	Bihar,	India	12737	ICWR SEL. 9168	Kitui,	Kenya
8869	ICWR SEL. 7942	Karnataka,	India	12738	ICWR SEL. 9175	Kitui,	Kenya
10957	AWR 74/15	Uttar Pradesh,	India	12739	ICWR SEL. 9213	Maharashtra,	India
10958	ICWR SEL. BANDA PALERA	Uttar Pradesh,	India	12740	ICWR SEL. 9229	Bihar,	India
10960	ICWR SEL. PURPLE 1	Uttar Pradesh,	India	12741	ICWR SEL. 9255		Burma
11286	ICWR SEL. T 17	Uttar Pradesh,	India	12742	ICWR SEL. 9758	New Delhi,	India
11287	ICWR SEL. 3753	Madhya Pradesh,	India	12743	ICWR SEL. 9858	Maharashtra,	India
11288	ICWR SEL. JA 274	Madhya Pradesh,	India	12744	ICWR SEL. 10269	New Delhi,	India
11289	ICWR SEL. 4769	Madhya Pradesh,	India	12745	ICWR SEL. 10517	Uttar Pradesh,	India
11290	ICWR SEL. 5097	Bihar,	India	12746	ICWR SEL. GP 125D	Uttar Pradesh,	India
11291	ICWR SEL. 6831	Uttar Pradesh,	India	12747	ICWR SEL. GP 126B	Uttar Pradesh,	India
11292	ICWR SEL. C 11	Maharashtra,	India	12748	ICWR SEL. C.NO74342[2]		
11293	ICWR SEL. No. 148	Maharashtra,	India	12749	ICWR SEL. C.NO74360[2]		
11294	ICWR SEL. BDN 1	Maharashtra,	India	12750	ICWR SEL. C.NO74362[2]		
11295	ICWR SEL. KWR 1	Uttar Pradesh,	India	12751	ICWR SEL. C 11 (BDN)(BROWN)	Maharashtra,	India
11296	ICWR SEL. HY 3A	Andhra Pradesh,	India	12752	ICWR SEL. C 11 (BDN)(WHITE)	Maharashtra,	India
11297	ICWR SEL. 7336	Madhya Pradesh,	India	12753	ICWR SEL. K 70	Uttar Pradesh,	India
11298	ICWR SEL. 7867	Karnataka,	India	12754	ICWR SEL. D2-73081[2]		
11299	ICWR SEL. BORI 1	Maharashtra,	India	12755	ICWR SEL. MAU-E 175	Maharashtra,	India
12725	ICWR SEL. 238	Andhra Pradesh,	India	12756	ICWR SEL. BSMR 1	Maharashtra	India
12726	ICWR SEL. 673	Maharashtra,	India	12757	ICWR SEL. PI 394568	Bihar,	India
				12758	ICWR SEL. PI 394954	New Delhi,	India
				12759	ICWR SEL. PI 395272	Andhra Pradesh,	India
				12760	ICWR SEL. BDN 1 (JBR)	Maharashtra,	India

1. Unknown   2. Source: ICRISAT.

Classification of sterility mosaic resistant accessions is given in Table 57.

Accessions with broad-based resistance to SM are ICP 999, 7353, 10977, 7867, 10976. They are found to be resistant at many locations in India. ICP 7867 also has resistance to wilt.

Classification of accessions resistant to phytophthora blight and a list of resistant genotypes follow (Tables 58 and 59).

Table 57. Maturity classification of pigeonpea accessions resistant to sterility mosaic disease.

Maturity group	No. of accessions
III	3
IV	3
V	11
VI	31
VII	63
VIII	109
IX	106
Total	326

ICP numbers of accessions resistant to sterility mosaic

2630	3782	3783	4344	4725	6630	6986
6997	7035	7119	7188	7201	7250	7349
7403	7428	7480	7867	7869	7871	7873
7898	7904	7906	7994	7997	8004	8006
8051	8077	8113	8120	8136	8145	8466
8501	8850	8852	8853	8856	8857	8861
9134	9136	9139	9140	9142	9144	9150
9155	9166	9182	9183	9187	9689	10222
10231	10235	10505	10976	to	11242	

Table 58. Maturity classification of pigeonpea accessions resistant to phytophthora blight (*Phytophthora drechsleri* f.sp *cajani*).

Maturity group	No. of accessions
I	1
III	3
IV	13
V	15
VI	26
VII	12
VIII	63
IX	7
Total	140

ICP numbers of accessions resistant to phytophthora blight

28	113	231	339	580	752	913
934	1088	1090	1120	1123	1149	1150
1151	1258	1321	1529	1535	1586	1788
1950	2153	2376	2505	2673	2682	2719
2736	2974	3008	3259	3367	3741	3753
3840	3861	3867	3868	3891	3899	3937
3945	4135	4141	4168	4699	4752	4882
5450	5860	6865	6952	6953	6956	6974
7057	7065	7151	7182	7185	7200	7232
7269	7273	7414	7533	7624	7657	7701
7754	7795	7798	7810	7837	7910	8087
8101	8103	8104	8110	8117	8122	8124
8131	8141	8144	8147	8149	8151	8214
8236	8248	8258	8282	8287	8289	8328
8332	8466	8557	8558	8559	8560	8562
8564	8568	8579	8603	8610	8619	8675
8688	8692	8700	8701	8756	8805	8865
8920	8921	9046	9059	9080	9103	9193
9196	9199	9206	9218	9247	9248	9250
9252	11300	11301	11302	11303	11304	11305

Table 59. Pigeonpea accessions with multiple-disease resistance/tolerance.

Lines with combined resistance/tolerance to	ICP number
Four diseases	
Wilt, sterility mosaic[1], root knot, and alternaria blight	8861, 8862
Three diseases	
Wilt, sterility mosaic[2], and phytophthora blight[3]	5097, 8094, ICPX 74360 progenies
Wilt, sterility mosaic[2], and root knot	8860, 11291
Wilt, alternaria blight, and bacterial blight	8863
Wilt, phytophthora blight[3], and root knot	8865, 8866
Wilt, sterility mosaic[2], and alternaria blight	8867, 8869, 10960, 11288, 11296
Two diseases	
Phytophthora blight[3] and alternaria blight	2376, 2719
Sterility mosaic[2] and alternaria blight	2630, 4725, 7188, 7869, 7904, 7906, 8850, 8856, 8857
Sterility mosaic[2] and phytophthora blight[3]	8466, 11300, 11301, 11302, 11303, 11304
Wilt and root knot	8859, 11286, 11299
Wilt and phytophthora blight[3]	8868, 10958, 11287, 11294
Wilt and sterility mosaic[2]	11289, 11290, 11297, 11298

1. Resistant except in the Indian states of Bihar and Tamil Nadu.
2. Resistant except in the Indian states of Bihar, Karnataka, and Tamil Nadu. ICP 10976 can be used for resistance to sterility mosaic in all Indian states.
3. Resistant to the P_2 isolate only.

Nematode diseases

Recently, ICRISAT identified seven parasitic nematode species on pigeonpea and initiated screening of germplasm against nematodes (ICRISAT 1985).

Nematode-resistant accessions include:
ICP 8859, 8860, 8861, 8862, 8865, 8866, 11286, 11291, and 11299.

Insect pests

Pest damage is considered as the most important problem at the farm level (Byth 1981). Surveys carried out by ICRISAT reveal that less than 10% of the farmers' fields that were visited had been protected by insecticide. Hence host plant resistance is of critical importance in pigeonpea improvement.

The major pests which severely affect the crop in the field are pod borer [*Heliothis armigera* (Hb.)] and podfly (*Melanagromyza obtusa* Mall.).

Screenings against these pests and subsequent purifications carried out by the entomologists and breeders at ICRISAT have resulted in identification of several sources of tolerance to these pests (Tables 60-62).

Pod borer and podfly tolerant accessions:
ICP 11961, 13197, 13201, and 13207

Table 60. Some characteristics of pod borer (*Heliothis armigera*) tolerant pigeonpea accessions.

ICP number	Maturity group	Growth habit[1]	Seed color[2]	100-seed mass (g)
11953	VIII	SS	O	8.5
11958	VII	SS	O	7.9
11959	IX	SS	C	7.0
11961	VII	SS	O	6.6
11962	IX	C	LB	7.7
11964	V	SS	O	9.9
11966	VI	SS	O	8.1
11967	VI	SS	O	7.9
13197	VIII	SS	O	10.7
13198	VI	SS	O	8.9
13199	VII	SS	C	10.4
13200	VIII	C	C	15.1
13201	VIII	C	C	9.1
13202	VII	SS	DB	9.0
13205	VIII	C	O	10.0
13206	VIII	C	LB	10.6
13207	III	SS	DB	9.8
13208	VIII	C	C+LB	8.7
13209	VI	SS	O	9.6
13212	VIII	SS	O	8.7
13214	VIII	SS	LB	9.3
13216	VIII	C	LB	9.5

1. C = Compact, SS = Semi-spreading.
2. C = Cream, DB = Dark brown, LB = Light brown, O = Orange.

Table 61. Some characteristics of podfly (*Melanagronyza obtusa*) tolerant pigeonpea accessions.

ICP number	Maturity group	Growth habit[1]	Seed color[2]	100-seed mass (g)
11950	VI	SS	O	7.0
11951	VIII	C	LB	7.8
11957	VIII	SS	C	7.9
11961	VII	SS	O	6.6
11965	VI	SS	C	8.4
11968	VI	SS	O	6.4
11969	VIII	C	C	8.2
11970	VIII	C	LB	7.6
11971	VII	S	O	6.0
11972	VIII	SS	O	5.5
13197	VIII	SS	O	10.7
13201	VIII	C	C	9.1
13203	VI	SS	O	8.5
13204	VI	SS	LB	11.5
13207	III	SS	DB	9.8
13210	VI	SS	C	11.1
13211	VI	SS	DB	9.4
13213	III	SS	DB	9.0
13215	VI	SS	B	7.1

1. C = Compact, SS = Semi-spreading.
2. B = Brown, C = Cream, DB = Dark brown, LB = Light brown, O = Orange.

Table 62. Insect tolerant pigeonpea accessions.

ICP number	Pedigree	Origin of material (Indian state)	Resistant/tolerant
11950	2223-1 E8-3EB	Andhra Pradesh	Podfly
11951	3615 E1-3EB	Maharashtra	Podfly
11953	5036 E1-3EB	Uttar Pradesh	Pod borer
11957	8094-2 S2X	Bihar	Podfly
11958	8325 E1-2EB	-[1]	Pod borer
11959	8606	Uttar Pradesh	Pod borer
11961	10466 E3-2EB	Andhra Pradesh	Pod borer + podfly
11962	PPE 36-2	Bihar	Pod borer
11964	PPE 45-2-3E[2]	-	Pod borer
11965	1691	Andhra Pradesh	Podfly
11966	1903 E1-3EB	Andhra Pradesh	Pod borer
11967	3328 E1-3EB	Karnataka	Pod borer
11968	6840 E1-3EB	Uttar Pradesh	Podfly
11969	7176-5 E1-3EB	Andhra Pradesh	Podfly
11970	7194-1 S4X 2EB	West Bengal	Podfly
11971	7941 E1-3EB	Karnataka	Podfly
11972	7946 E1-3EB	Karnataka	Podfly
13197	ICP 8102-5 S1X 6EB	Bihar	Pod borer + podfly
13198	ICP 4070 E2-5EB	Andhra Pradesh	Pod borer
13199	ICP 9001 E3-5EB	Gujarat	Pod borer
13200	ICP 7337-2 S4X 6EB	Madhya Pradesh	Pod borer
13201	ICP 7537 E1-5EB	Madhya Pradesh	Pod borer + podfly
13202	ICP 8229 E1-6EB	-	Pod borer
13203	ICP 1811 E3-5EB	Andhra Pradesh	Podfly
13204	ICP 3009 E3-5EB	Andhra Pradesh	Podfly
13205	ICP 4745-2 E8-5EB	Madhya Pradesh	Pod borer
13206	ICP 8127 E3-5EB	Bihar	Pod borer
13207	ICP 909 E3-5EB	Uttar Pradesh	Pod borer + podfly
13208	ICP 8595 E1-6EB	Uttar Pradesh	Pod borer
13209	ICP 810 E1-5EB	Andhra Pradesh	Pod borer
13210	GS 1-4EB	Karnataka	Podfly

Continued

Table 62 *Continued*

ICP number	Pedigree	Origin of material (Indian state)	Resistant/tolerant
13211	AGR 20B 4EB	Madhya Pradesh	Podfly
13212	ICP 8583 E1-6EB	Uttar Pradesh	Pod borer
13213	SEHORE 197-5EB	Madhya Pradesh	Podfly
13214	GW 3-5EB	Madhya Pradesh	Por borer
13215	ICP 7050-6EB	Madhya Pradesh	Podfly
13216	PPE 37-3-6B	Bihar	Pod borer

1. Source unknown.   2. Source: ICRISAT.

Germplasm of Special Interest

Widely used cultivars

Systematic characterization and evaluation resulted in the identification of several landraces with desirable agronomic traits. These are frequently used as parents in pigeonpea improvement programs. Similarly the standard cultivars, which were developed at various centers are also frequently used by breeders in experiments and trials. The classification and listing of these are given in Tables 63 and 64.

Table 63. Standard pigeonpea cultivars/landraces in 0-IX maturity groups widely used in crop improvement.

Group	Cultivars	Group	Cultivars	Group	Cultivars
0	1	IV	3	VIII	45
I	2	V	16	IX	12
II	7	VI	35		
III	4	VII	25	Total	150

Table 64. Identity and accession numbers (ICP) of widely used standard pigeonpea cultivars/landraces.

Maturity group	Identity	ICP No.	Maturity group	Identity	ICP No.
0	PANT A 3	6974	V *continued*	S.A 1	7607
				BDN 2	7623
I	PANT A 2	6973		T 28	7718
	PRABHAT	7220		ANM 436	8081
				KMR 6	8508
II	UPAS 120	6971		FIELD COLL.	8871
	PANT A 1	6972			
	DSLR 38	7018	VI	SHARDA SEL.	1
	DSLR 45	7025		P 4280	450
	DSLR 98	7078		ST 1	1621
	PANT A 8	7179		P 3888	2376
	PANT A 9	7180		SHARDA	2626
				MUKTA	2627
III	T 21	26		P 1181-1	2812
	PUSA AGETI	28		P 537-32-1	4720
	DSLR 125	7105		P 4337	5444
	EC 109884	7135		JA 277	6393
IV	P 2812	6		P 2287	6523
	DSLR 22	7002		P 2288	6524
	KMR 1	8513		P 2290	6526
				EC 107644	6899
V	P 4787-1	504		EC 107654	6909
	P 3724	3773		CODE NO. 2	6914
	EC 107647	6902		CODE NO. 3	6915
	CODE NO. 5	6917		CODE NO. 4	6916
	CODE NO. 19	6930		CODE NO. 18	6929
	DSLR 108	7088		CODE NO. 29	6969
	NO. 148	7120			
	BDN 1	7182		DSLR 6	6986
	HY 4	7191		DSLR 17	6997
	HYB 2	7222		C 11	7118

Continued

Table 64 *Continued*

Maturity group	Identity	ICP No.	Maturity group	Identity	ICP No.
VI continued	PS 41	7183	VII continued	ANM 280	7894
	PS 54	7186		ANM 330	7952
	PS 65	7189		GC 6800-67	8466
	PS 71	7190		LRG 30	8518
	JA 3	7193		LJR 93	8982
	PDM 1	7218		PURPLE 1	10960
	UQ 50	7263			
	ANM 79	7409	VIII	P 4685/1	102
	P 15-3-3	7626		P 4122-1	999
	PLA 366	8257		P 1129	2795
	FIELD COLL.	8870		JA 274	3782
	CSS 1	10004		P 442	4234
				P 220	4782
VII	P 1794-2	1258		T 7	6344
	T 17	1641		JA 276	6392
	P 2096	2290		P 2275	6520
	GRANADA	2628			
	P 300-20-1	3682		EC 107636	6891
	JA 275	3783		EC 107652	6907
	P 1062/1	4395		EC 107657	6912
	JA 278-1	4726		CODE NO. 14	6926
	P 207-121-1	4780		AS 29	6967
	EC 100465	6399		BRAZIL 465	6975
				DSLR 56	7036
	EC 107638	6893		DSLR 85	7065
	EC 107647	6902		DSLR 106	7086
	DSLR 22	7002		PS 43	7184
	DSLR 55	7035		PS 66	7188
	HY 3C	7119		ANM 292	7906
	UQ 34	7249		ANM 324B	7942
	AS 71-37	7855		ANM 351A	7979
	ANM 252	7867		ANM 439	8084
	ANM 261	7875		ANM 461	8106

Continued

Table 64 *Continued*

Maturity group	Identity	ICP No.
VIII *continued*	ANM 467	8113
	ANM 475	8121
	ANM 479	8126
	ANM 484	8131
	ANM 493	8140
	ANM 500	8147
	ANM 510	8157
	ANM 513	8160
	PLA 266	8221
	PLA 332	8242
	PLA 365	8256
	PLA 367	8258
	PLA 432	8280
	PLA 520	8301
	PLA 557	8310
	PLS 351/2A	8442
	TTB 7	8501
	A C 314 (WHITE)	8504
	K 3	8516
	ICWR 7	8864
IX	NP 69	4779
	NP(WR) 15	6443
	EC 107642	6897
	PS 54	7186
	P 1258	7197
	KWR 1	7198
	K 23	7199
	K 16	7200
	GWALIOR 3	7221
	ANM 460	8105
	K 73	8464
	JM 2412	9150

Lines developed at ICRISAT

As a result of team work over several years, ICRISAT has developed several elite lines in different maturity groups. This is a continuous process and some of the important lines developed at ICRISAT are classified and listed in Tables 65 and 66.

Table 65. Maturity classification of pigeonpea lines (ICPLs) developed at ICRISAT.

Maturity group	No. of accessions
0	5
I	9
II	40
III	24
IV	15
V	20
VI	114
VII	20
VIII	5
IX	3
Total	255

Table 66. Accession numbers (ICP numbers) of lines (ICPLs) developed at ICRISAT.

ICPL No.	ICP No.	ICPL No.	ICP No.	ICPL No.	ICP No.	ICPL No.	ICP No.
Group 0		**Group II**		**Group III**		**Group IV**	
82	11538	141	11595	5	11498	31	11523
83	11539	144	11598	9	11502	105	11561
159	11613	145	11599	84	11540	162	11616
161	11615	146	11600	87	11543	181	11635
185	11639	151	11605	91	11547	189	11643
287	11737	153	11607	140	11594	198	11652
		155	11609	142	11596	200	11654
Group I		156	11610	148	11602	207	11661
143	11597	158	11612	152	11606	288	11738
147	11601	163	11617	154	11608	290	11740
174	11628	164	11618	160	11614		
179	11633	167	11621	165	11619	**Group V**	
180	11634	168	11622	166	11620	21	11514
183	11637	169	11623	170	11624	30	11522
267	11717	171	11625	182	11636	33	11525
268	11718	172	11626	193	11647	35	11527
289	11739	173	11627	194	11648	37	11529
		175	11629	199	11653	108	11564
Group II		176	11630	202	11656	109	11565
		177	11631	203	11657	112	11568
2	11495	178	11632	204	11658	114	11570
11	11504	184	11638	205	11659	116	11572
83	11539	186	11640	206	11660	117	11573
85	11541	187	11641	291	11741	119	11575
86	11542	188	11642			123	11579
88	11544	201	11655			129	11585
89	11545	208	11662	**Group IV**		149	11603
90	11546	269	11719	7	11500	150	11604
92	11548	292	11742	8	11501	210	11664
93	11549			12	11505	212	11666
94	11550			18	11511	249	11703
				20	11513	296	11746

Continued

Table 66 *Continued*

ICPL No.	ICP No.	ICPL No.	ICP No.	ICPL No.	ICP No.	ICPL No.	ICP No.
Group VI		**Group VI**		**Group VI**		**Group VI**	
13	11506	115	11571	231	11685	284	11734
14	11507	118	11574	232	11686	285	11735
15	11508	120	11576	233	11687	286	11736
16	11509	121	11577	234	11688	293	11743
17	11510	122	11578	235	11689	294	11744
19	11512	124	11580	239	11693	295	11745
22	11515	125	11581	240	11694	297	11747
23	11516	127	11583	241	11695	298	11748
24	11517	128	11584	242	11696	299	11749
25	11518	130	11586	243	11697	300	11750
26	11519	131	11587	244	11698	301	11751
27	11520	132	11588	245	11699	302	11752
28	11521	133	11589	247	11701	303	11753
32	11524	138	11592	248	11702	304	11754
34	11526	139	11593	255	11707	305	11755
36	11528	157	11611	258	11708	306	11756
38	11530	209	11663	260	11710	307	11757
39	11531	211	11665	261	11711	308	11758
40	11532	213	11667	262	11712	309	11759
41	11533	215	11669	263	11713		
53	11536	217	11671	266	11716	**Group VII**	
95	11551	219	11673	270	11720		
98	11554	220	11674	272	11722	42	11534
99	11555	221	11675	273	11723	43	11535
101	11557	222	11676	275	11725	96	11552
102	11558	223	11677	276	11726	97	11553
103	11559	224	11678	277	11727	136	11590
104	11560	225	11679	278	11728	190	11644
107	11563	226	11680	279	11729	191	11645
111	11567	228	11682	281	11731	192	11646
113	11569	229	11683	282	11732	214	11668
		230	11684	283	11733	216	11670
						218	11672

Continued

Table 66 *Continued*

ICPL No.	ICP No.		ICPL No.	ICP No.
Group VII			**Group VIII**	
227	11681		137	11591
236	11690		246	11700
237	11691		250	11704
238	11692		251	11705
264	11714		254	11706
265	11715			
271	11721		**Group IX**	
274	11724		259	11709
280	11730		310	11760
			311	11761

Ten broad germplasm composites

Ten germplasm pools were constituted from 3480 accessions grown in 1973/74. The purpose was to reduce the number of lines in germplasm and use composites of similar types as source material.

Some characteristics of the groups are given in Table 67. The groups have been grown every year under isolation for 11 years and seed is available for distribution.

Accessions from arid areas

Pigeonpea is basically a drought-tolerant plant. There is every possibility of genotypic differences existing in this important trait. However, so far

Table 67. Number, source, and some characteristics of pigeonpea germplasm collections placed in ten broad groups.

Group	No. of cultures	Source	Plant type	Height	100-seed mass (g)	Days to 50% flowering
1	1	India	Compact	Short	7.90	80.3
2	24	India	Spreading + semi-spreading	Medium	7.76	85.9
3	14	India	Compact	Tall + medium	7.20	118.4
4	1594	India	Semi-spreading	Tall + medium	7.23	111.1
5	1253	India	Spreading	Tall + medium	7.38	103.2
6	11	India	Spreading + semi-spreading	-		
	25	Puerto Rico			14.35	131.6
7	46	India	Spreading + semi-spreading	Short	8.08	97.2
8	68	India	Compact	Tall + medium	8.44	150.8
9	9	India	Spreading + semi-spreading	Short	7.84	143.7
10	435	India	Spreading + semi-spreading	Tall	7.71	144.0

there are no comprehensive data available on a systematic screening of germplasm for this trait. Preliminary observations indicate that long-duration cultivars in general have a deep tap-root system, which sustains the crop on residual moisture. Accessions originating from arid areas are listed in Table 68.

Pigeonpeas are generally highly susceptible to frost. In India and Java productive plants were found at altitudes up to 1830 m, but seed set was adversely affected at 1020 to 1525 m in Hawaii, where minimum night temperature was 10°C (Akinola, et al. 1975). However, in Kenya even at 1500 m pigeonpea performs satisfactorily, as the area is located close to the equator. Accessions originating from high altitudes are listed in Table 70.

Table 68. Pigeonpea accessions from arid areas of India, donated by JNKV[1].

ICP No.	Pedigree
Accessions from Rajasthan	
8738	AJMER 1
8739	AJMER 2
8740	AJMER 3
8741	AJMER 4
8742	AJMER 5
8743	AJMER 6
8744	AJMER 7
Accessions from Haryana	
8800	HISAR 1
8801	HISAR 2
8802	HISAR 3
8803	HISAR 4
8804	HISAR 5
8805	HISAR 6
8806	HISAR 7
8807	HISAR 8

1. JNKV = Jawaharlal Nehru Krishi Viswa Vidyalaya.

Accessions from acid soils

Pigeonpea grows satisfactorily on soil with a pH of 5 to 8 (Akinola et al. 1975). Systematic screening of germplasm for acid-soil tolerance has not yet been undertaken. Preliminary experiments indicate that the following lines possess tolerance.

Accessions originating from districts having predominantly acid soils are listed in Table 69.

Table 69. Accessions from districts with predominantly acid soils.

ICP No.	Pedigree	Country[1]	Province/State	Location	Collector/Donor[3]
4027	P 1188/1	BRA	-[2]	-	IARI
4406	P 1188	BRA	-	-	IARI
5433	P 3727	BRA	-	-	BERH
5479	P 4641	IND	Orissa	Maliguda/Koraput	NAYA
5481	P 4642	IND	Orissa	Maliguda/Koraput	NAYA
5482	P 4642-1	IND	Orissa	Maliguda/Koraput	NAYA
5484	P 4642/1	IND	Orissa	Maliguda/Koraput	NAYA
5764	P 4645/1	IND	Orissa	Bandugaon/Koraput	NAYA
6314	P 4643	IND	Orissa	Bengal Bada/Koraput	NAYA
6315	P 4645	IND	Orissa	Khangaon/Koraput	NAYA
6975	BRAZIL 465	BRA	-	-	-
6986	DSLR 6	IND	Orissa	Saloor-Jeypore Road/Koraput	DSLR
6987	DSLR 7	IND	Orissa	Kundali/Koraput	DSLR
6988	DLSR 8	IND	Orissa	Dhollium/Koraput	DSLR
6989	DSLR 9	IND	Orissa	Koraput/Koraput	DSLR
6990	DSLR 10	IND	Orissa	Jeypore/Koraput	DSLR
6991	DSLR 11	IND	Orissa	Kotapad/Koraput	DSLR
7117	BRAZIL 465-1	BRA	-	-	APAU
7264	UQ 51	BRA	-	-	UQ
7324	ANM 3	IND	Madhya Pradesh	Bataikela/Raigarh	ANM
7331	ANM 10	IND	Madhya Pradesh	Thotla/Raigarh	ANM
7333	ANM 12	IND	Madhya Pradesh	Kataibela/Raigarh	ANM
7336	ANM 15	IND	Madhya Pradesh	Baghicha/Raigarh	ANM
7339	ANM 18	IND	Madhya Pradesh	Baghicha/Raigarh	ANM
7344	ANM 23	IND	Madhya Pradesh	Dhansara/Raigarh	ANM
7345	ANM 24	IND	Madhya Pradesh	Sarangarh/Raigarh	ANM
7346	ANM 25	IND	Madhya Pradesh	Sarangarh/Raigarh	ANM

Continued

Table 69 *Continued*

ICP No.	Province/Pedigree	Country[1]	State	Location	Collector/Donor
7350	ANM 29	IND	Madhya Pradesh	Surteli/Bilaspur	ANM
7351	ANM 30A	IND	Madhya Pradesh	Dhansara/Raigarh	ANM
7352	ANM 30B	IND	Madhya Pradesh	Dhansara/Raigarh	ANM
7353	ANM 31	IND	Madhya Pradesh	Thotla/Raigarh	ANM
7377	ANM 46	IND	Madhya Pradesh	Baghicha/Raigarh	ANM
7380	ANM 49	IND	Madhya Pradesh	Sannakunkum/Raigarh	ANM
7403	ANM 73	IND	Madhya Pradesh	Kunkeri/Raigarh	ANM
7408	ANM 78	IND	Madhya Pradesh	Baghicha/Raigarh	ANM
7411	ANM 81	IND	Madhya Pradesh	Dhansara/Raigarh	ANM
7413	ANM 83	IND	Madhya Pradesh	Baghichapahadi/Raigarh	ANM
7414	ANM 84	IND	Madhya Pradesh	Kasayya/Raigarh	ANM
7417	ANM 87	IND	Madhya Pradesh	Kasayya/Raigarh	ANM
7438	ANM 102	IND	Madhya Pradesh	Bataikela/Raigarh	ANM
7442	ANM 106	IND	Madhya Pradesh	Rowni/Raigarh	ANM
7448	ANM 112	IND	Madhya Pradesh	Durgapada/Raigarh	ANM
7618	FIELD COLL.	IND	Orissa	Rayagarh	JNKV
7898	ANM 284	IND	Karnataka	Chikka Bagil/Mysore	ANM
7899	ANM 285	IND	Karnataka	Putgana Halli/Mysore	ANM
7990	ANM 357	IND	Orissa	Rayagarh/Koraput	ANM
7991	ANM 358A	IND	Orissa	Bisamcuttak/Koraput	ANM
7992	ANM 358B	IND	Orissa	Bisamcuttak/Koraput	ANM
7993	ANM 358C	IND	Orissa	Bisamcuttak/Koraput	ANM
7994	ANM 359A	IND	Orissa	Muniguda/Koraput	ANM
7995	ANM 359B	IND	Orissa	Muniguda/Koraput	ANM
7996	ANM 360	IND	Orissa	Dhodavali/Phulbani	ANM
7997	ANM 361A	IND	Orissa	Kotagarh/Phulbani	ANM
7998	ANM 361B	IND	Orissa	Kotagarh/Phulbani	ANM

Continued

Table 69 *Continued*

ICP No.	Pedigree	Country[1]	Province/State	Location	Collector/Donor
7999	ANM 362	IND	Orissa	Kotagarh/Phulbani	ANM
8000	ANM 363	IND	Orissa	Kotagarh/Phulbani	ANM
8001	ANM 364	IND	Orissa	Kotagarh/Phulbani	ANM
8002	ANM 365A	IND	Orissa	Baliguda/Phulbani	ANM
8003	ANM 365B	IND	Orissa	Baliguda/Phulbani	ANM
8004	ANM 366A	IND	Orissa	Phiringia/Phulbani	ANM
8005	ANM 366B	IND	Orissa	Phiringia/Phulbani	ANM
8006	ANM 367	IND	Orissa	Phiringia/Phulbani	ANM
8013	ANM 374	IND	Orissa	Birgovindpur/Keonjhar	ANM
8014	ANM 375	IND	Orissa	Harichandanapur/Keonjhar	ANM
8015	ANM 376	IND	Orissa	Harichandanapur/Keonjhar	ANM
8016	ANM 377	IND	Orissa	Dhonekote/Keonjhar	ANM
8017	ANM 378	IND	Orissa	Badphosi/Keonjhar	ANM
8025	ANM 385	IND	Bihar	Bewa/Santal Parganas	ANM
8027	ANM 387	IND	Bihar	Palajar/Santal Parganas	ANM
8028	ANM 388	IND	Bihar	Raganathpur/Santal Parganas	ANM
8038	ANM 398	IND	Bihar	Tutilava/Hazaribagh	ANM
8067	ANM 422	IND	Orissa	Padwa/Koraput	ANM
8068	ANM 423	IND	Orissa	Padwa/Koraput	ANM
8074	ANM 429	IND	Orissa	Harichandanpur/Keonjhar	ANM
8076	ANM 431	IND	Orissa	Borigaon/Keonjhar	ANM
8077	ANM 432	IND	Orissa	Anandpur/Keonjhar	ANM
8089	ANM 444	IND	Bihar	Hansdoha/Santal Parganas	ANM
8153	ANM 506	IND	Bihar	Jumgama/Gaya	ANM
8154	ANM 507	IND	Bihar	Tekuna/Gaya	ANM
8155	ANM 508	IND	Bihar	Mahulal/Gaya	ANM
8156	ANM 509	IND	Bihar	Karmoni/Gaya	ANM

Continued

Table 69 *Continued*

ICP No.	Pedigree	Country[1]	Province/State	Location	Collector/Donor
8157	ANM 510	IND	Bihar	Orma/Gaya	ANM
8158	ANM 511	IND	Bihar	Gurandi/Hazaribagh	ANM
8159	ANM 512	IND	Bihar	Gangri/Hazaribagh	ANM
8160	ANM 513	IND	Bihar	Raketh/Hazaribagh	ANM
8161	ANM 514	IND	Bihar	Chatra/Hazaribagh	ANM
8162	ANM 515	IND	Bihar	Leapu/Hazaribagh	ANM
8348	ANM 535	IND	Tamil Nadu	Parthiputhur/N. Arcot	ANM
8349	ANM 536	IND	Tamil Nadu	Uppupet/N. Arcot	ANM
8350	ANM 537	IND	Tamil Nadu	Aroor/N. Arcot	ANM
8358	ANM 545	IND	Tamil Nadu	Tiruvannamalai/N.Arcot	ANM
8359	ANM 546	IND	Tamil Nadu	Kstatesattampoondi/N.Arcot	ANM
8398	ANM 592	IND	Kerala	Vandithaualam/Palghat	ANM
8399	ANM 594	IND	Kerala	Vandithaualam/Palghat	ANM
8400	ANM 595	IND	Kerala	Pattancheri/Palghat	ANM
8401	ANM 596	IND	Kerala	Tatamaragalam/Palghat	ANM
8412	ANM 607	IND	Tamil Nadu	Erralli (Dharmapuri)/Salem	ANM
8413	ANM 608	IND	Tamil Nadu	Erralli (Dharmapuri)/Salem	ANM
8414	ANM 609	IND	Tamil Nadu	Savalpatti (Dharmapuri)/Salem	ANM
8415	ANM 610	IND	Tamil Nadu	Savalpatti (Dharmapuri)/Salem	ANM
8416	ANM 611	IND	Tamil Nadu	Kothaver (Dharmapuri)/Salem	ANM
8417	ANM 612	IND	Tamil Nadu	Nagampatti (Dharmapuri)/Salem	ANM
8418	ANM 613	IND	Tamil Nadu	Audhanapet (Dharmapuri)/Salem	ANM
8419	ANM 614	IND	Tamil Nadu	Kalathupatti (Dharmapuri)/Salem	ANM
8420	ANM 615	IND	Tamil Nadu	Periagaram/N. Arcot	ANM
8421	ANM 616	IND	Tamil Nadu	Mandvadi/N. Arcot	ANM

Continued

Table 69 *Continued*

ICP No.	Pedigree	Country[1]	Province/State	Location	Collector/Donor
8521	ANM 617	IND	Tamil Nadu	Vadepadupatti/N. Arcot	ANM
8522	ANM 618	IND	Tamil Nadu	Elavambadi/N. Arcot	ANM
8523	ANM 619	IND	Tamil Nadu	Prajapuram/N. Arcot	ANM
8524	ANM 620	IND	Tamil Nadu	Serpadi/N. Arcot	ANM
8525	ANM 621	IND	Tamil Nadu	Serpadi/N. Arcot	ANM
8526	ANM 622	IND	Tamil Nadu	Asanamhutti/N. Arcot	ANM
8527	ANM 623	IND	Tamil Nadu	Talavaipatari/N. Arcot	ANM
8528	ANM 624	IND	Tamil Nadu	Vishwasampatti (Dharmapuri)	ANM
8529	ANM 625	IND	Tamil Nadu	Channappanayakanur (Dharmapuri)	ANM
8530	ANM 626	IND	Tamil Nadu	Jogipatti (Dharmapuri)/Salem	ANM
8531	ANM 627	IND	Tamil Nadu	Denkanikottai (Dharmapuri)/Salem	ANM
8532	ANM 628	IND	Tamil Nadu	Bikkanahalli (Dharmapuri)/Salem	ANM
8533	ANM 629	IND	Tamil Nadu	Bikkanahalli (Dharmapuri)/Salem	ANM
8534	ANM 630	IND	Tamil Nadu	Bikkanahalli (Dharmapuri)/Salem	ANM
8537	ANM 634	IND	Orissa	Mundiguda/Koraput	ANM
8538	ANM 635	IND	Orissa	Mundiguda/Koraput	ANM
8539	ANM 637	IND	Orissa	Laxmipur/Koraput	ANM
8540	ANM 639	IND	Orissa	Kashipur/Koraput	ANM
8541	ANM 644	IND	Orissa	Kashipur/Koraput	ANM
8542	ANM 646	IND	Orissa	Tikri/Koraput	ANM
8543	ANM 647	IND	Orissa	Tikri/Koraput	ANM
8544	ANM 648	IND	Orissa	Semiabagudi/Koraput	ANM
8545	ANM 649	IND	Orissa	Ramanaguda/Koraput	ANM
8546	ANM 650	IND	Orissa	Gunupur/Koraput	ANM
8547	ANM 652	IND	Orissa	Bhalery/Koraput	ANM
8548	ANM 653	IND	Orissa	Papadahandy/Koraput	ANM
9277	PI 394890	LKA			USDA

Continued

Table 69 *Continued*

ICP No.	Pedigree	Country[1]	State	Province/Location	Collector/Donor
10001	JM 3094	IND	Kerala	Chitalli Palghat/Palghat	LJGM
10941	PR 4787	IND	Kerala	Palghat/Palghat	PR
10942	PR 4790	IND	Kerala	Payyallore/Palghat	PR
10948	PR 4871	IND	Orissa	Kasipur/Koraput	PR
11902	PR 5180	IND	Kerala	Chindakki/Palghat	PR
11903	PR 5181	IND	Kerala	Chindakki/Palghat	PR
11904	PR 5182	IND	Kerala	Chindakki/Palghat	PR
11905	PR 5183	IND	Kerala	Chindakki/Palghat	PR
11906	PR 5184	IND	Kerala	Chindakki/Palghat	PR
11907	PR 5185	IND	Kerala	Chindakki/Palghat	PR
11908	PR 5186	IND	Kerala	Chindakki/Palghat	PR
11909	PR 5187	IND	Kerala	Chindakki/Palghat	PR
11910	PR 5188	IND	Kerala	Chindakki/Palghat	PR
11911	PR 5189	IND	Kerala	Chindakki/Palghat	PR
11912	PR 5190	IND	Kerala	Kakkappadi/Palghat	PR
11913	PR 5191	IND	Kerala	Kalkandi/Palghat	PR
11914	PR 5191-1	IND	Kerala	Kalkandi/Palghat	PR
11915	PR 5192	IND	Kerala	Chemmanur/Palghat	PR
11916	PR 5193	IND	Kerala	Chemmanur/Palghat	PR
11917	PR 5194	IND	Kerala	Chemmanur/Palghat	PR
11918	PR 5195	IND	Kerala	Pakulam/Palghat	PR
11919	PR 5196	IND	Kerala	Pakulam/Palghat	PR
11920	PR 5197	IND	Kerala	Pakulam/Palghat	PR
11921	PR 5199	IND	Kerala	Karavadom/Palghat	PR
11922	PR 5203	IND	Kerala	Karavadom/Palghat	PR
11923	PR 5204	IND	Kerala	Karavangadi/Palghat	PR
11924	PR 5206	IND	Kerala	Kammandikal/Palghat	PR

Continued

Table 69 *Continued*

ICP No.	Pedigree	Country[1]	Province/State	Location	Collector/Donor
11925	PR 5208	IND	Kerala	Mannanthora/Palghat	PR
11926	PR 5209	IND	Kerala	Mannanthora/Palghat	PR
11927	PR 5210	IND	Kerala	Mannanthora/Palghat	PR
11928	PR 5211	IND	Kerala	Kadathara North/Palghat	PR
11929	PR 5212	IND	Kerala	Pattimala/Palghat	PR
11930	PR 5213	IND	Kerala	Pattimala/Palghat	PR
11931	PR 5219	IND	Kerala	Anakkatti/Palghat	PR
11932	PR 5246	IND	Kerala	Mukkali/Palghat	PR
12903	PR 6023	IND	Orissa	Peddumalaga/Koraput	PR
12912	PR 6028-1	IND	Orissa	Ramachandrapuram/Koraput	PR
12913	PR 6028-2	IND	Orissa	Ramachandrapuram/Koraput	PR
12914	PR 6029	IND	Orissa	Jagudipetta/Koraput	PR
12915	PR 6030-1	IND	Orissa	Rayagada/Koraput	PR
12916	PR 6030-2	IND	Orissa	Rayagada/Koraput	PR
12917	PR 6030-3	IND	Orissa	Rayagada/Koraput	PR
12918	PR 6032	IND	Orissa	Rayagada/Koraput	PR
12919	PR 6033	IND	Orissa	Kuttaguda/Koraput	PR
12920	PR 6035	IND	Orissa	Rayagada/Koraput	PR
12921	PR 6036	IND	Orissa	Kotuli/Koraput	PR
12922	PR 6037-1	IND	Orissa	Bursa/Koraput	PR
12923	PR 6037-2	IND	Orissa	Bursa/Koraput	PR
12924	PR 6037-3	IND	Orissa	Bursa/Koraput	PR
12925	PR 6040	IND	Orissa	Patharphu/Koraput	PR
12926	PR 6042	IND	Orissa	Dasaguda/Koraput	PR
12927	PR 6043	IND	Orissa	B.Guda/Koraput	PR
12928	PR 6044-1	IND	Orissa	Sava Colony/Koraput	PR
12929	PR 6044-2	IND	Orissa	Sava Colony/Koraput	PR

Continued

Table 69 *Continued*

ICP No.	Pedigree	Country[1]	Province/State	Location	Collector/Donor
12930	PR 6045	IND	Orissa	Malkangiri/Koraput	PR
12931	PR 6046	IND	Orissa	Shangadaon/Koraput	PR
12932	PR 6047	IND	Orissa	Malkangiri/Koraput	PR
12933	PR 6048	IND	Orissa	Malkangiri Dam/Koraput	PR
12934	PR 6049	IND	Orissa	Boriguma/Koraput	PR
12935	PR 6050	IND	Orissa	Jothigiri/Koraput	PR
12936	PR 6054	IND	Orissa	Bijapur/Koraput	PR
12941	PR 6061-1	IND	Orissa	Umarkote/Koraput	PR
12942	PR 6061-2	IND	Orissa	Umarkote/Koraput	PR
12943	PR 6062	IND	Orissa	Sanabharandi/Koraput	PR
12944	PR 6063-1	IND	Orissa	Umarkote/Koraput	PR
12945	PR 6063-2	IND	Orissa	Umarkote/Koraput	PR
12946	PR 6064	IND	Orissa	Suraguda/Koraput	PR
12947	PR 6065-1	IND	Orissa	Koraput/Koraput	PR
12948	PR 6065-2	IND	Orissa	Koraput/Koraput	PR
12949	PR 6066-1	IND	Orissa	Jataban/Koraput	PR
12950	PR 6066-2	IND	Orissa	Jataban/Koraput	PR
12951	PR 6067	IND	Orissa	Jataban/Koraput	PR
12952	PR 6068-1	IND	Orissa	Majigudga/Koraput	PR
12953	PR 6068-2	IND	Orissa	Majigudga/Koraput	PR
12954	PR 6068-3	IND	Orissa	Majigudga/Koraput	PR
12955	PR 6069-1	IND	Orissa	Parli/Koraput	PR
12956	PR 6069-2	IND	Orissa	Parli/Koraput	PR
12958	PR 6070-1	IND	Orissa	Boriguma/Koraput	PR
12959	PR 6072	IND	Orissa	Thomiguda/Koraput	PR
12960	PR 6073-1	IND	Orissa	Penta/Koraput	PR
12961	PR 6073-2	IND	Orissa	Penta/Koraput	PR

Continued

Table 69 *Continued*

ICP No.	Pedigree	Country[1]	Province/State	Location	Collector/Donor
12962	PR 6074	IND	Orissa	Penta/Koraput	PR
12963	PR 6075-1	IND	Orissa	Bissamcuttack/Koraput	PR
12964	PR 6075-2	IND	Orissa	Bissamcuttack/Koraput	PR
12965	PR 6075-3	IND	Orissa	Bissamcuttack/Koraput	PR
12966	PR 6076	IND	Orissa	Bissamcuttack/Koraput	PR
12967	PR 6077	IND	Orissa	Bissamcuttack/Koraput	PR
12968	PR 6078	IND	Orissa	Gujjalpur/Koraput	PR
12969	PR 6079	IND	Orissa	Badigadn/Koraput	PR
12970	PR 6080	IND	Orissa	Bassamcuttack/Koraput	PR
12971	PR 6081-1	IND	Orissa	Mundawadi/Koraput	PR
12972	PR 6081-2	IND	Orissa	Mundawadi/Koraput	PR
12973	PR 6081-3	IND	Orissa	Mundawadi/Koraput	PR
12974	PR 6082	IND	Orissa	Burguguda/Koraput	PR
12975	PR 6083	IND	Orissa	Burguguda/Koraput	PR
12997	PR 6103	IND	Orissa	Boudh/Phulabani	PR
12998	PR 6104	IND	Orissa	Boudh/Phulabani	PR
12999	PR 6105	IND	Orissa	Kamalpur/Phulabani	PR
13000	PR 6106	IND	Orissa	Babanda/Phulabani	PR
13001	PR 6107	IND	Orissa	Charkota/Phulabani	PR
13002	PR 6108-1	IND	Orissa	Madhupur/Phulabani	PR
13003	PR 6108-2	IND	Orissa	Madhupur/Phulabani	PR
13004	PR 6109-1	IND	Orissa	Madhupur/Phulabani	PR
13005	PR 6109-2	IND	Orissa	Madhupur/Phulabani	PR
13012	PR 6117	IND	Orissa	Baddiyabundh/Dhenkanal	PR
13013	PR 6118	IND	Orissa	Vikrantpur/Dhenkanal	PR
13014	PR 6119	IND	Orissa	Nangari/Dhenkanal	PR
13015	PR 6120	IND	Orissa	Budapunk/Dhenkanal	PR

Continued

Table 69 *Continued*

ICP No.	Pedigree	Country[1]	Province/State	Location	Collector/Donor
13016	PR 6121	IND	Orissa	Muhatta/Dhenkanal	PR
13017	PR 6122	IND	Orissa	Anugal/Dhenkanal	PR
13018	PR 6123	IND	Orissa	Rajmalpur/Dhenkanal	PR
13026	PR 6135-4	IND	Orissa	Mundergaon/Phulabani	PR
13027	PR 6136-5	IND	Orissa	Mundergaon/Phulabani	PR
13028	PR 6139-1	IND	Orissa	Dandra/Koraput	PR
13029	PR 6139-2	IND	Orissa	Dandra/Koraput	PR
13030	PR 6139-3	IND	Orissa	Dandra/Koraput	PR
13031	PR 6139-4	IND	Orissa	Dandra/Koraput	PR
13032	PR 6139-5	IND	Orissa	Dandra/Koraput	PR
13033	PR 6140-1	IND	Orissa	Hazaritang/Koraput	PR
13034	PR 6140-2	IND	Orissa	Hazaritang/Koraput	PR
13035	PR 6140-1	IND	Orissa	Hazaritang/Koraput	PR
13036	PR 6141	IND	Orissa	Baldaguda/Koraput	PR
13037	PR 6142	IND	Orissa	Ramanaguda/Koraput	PR
13038	PR 6143-2	IND	Orissa	Ramanaguda/Koraput	PR
13039	PR 6144-3	IND	Orissa	Penakkam/Koraput	PR
13040	PR 6145	IND	Orissa	Narayanaguda/Koraput	PR
13041	PR 6146	IND	Orissa	Kujindri/Koraput	PR

1. BRA = Brazil, IND = India, LKA = Sri Lanka.
2. Unknown.
3. A complete list of these initials is given in the companion volume — ICRISAT Pigeonpea Germplasm Catalog: Passport Information.

Table 70. Pigeonpea accessions from altitudes >1000 m.

ICP No.	Pedigree	Country[1]	Province/ State	Location	Collector/ Donor
9131	JM 2377	KEN	Eastern	Kimutwa/Machakos	LJGM
9132	JM 2379	KEN	Eastern	Kimutwa/Machakos	LJGM
9133	JM 2380	KEN	Eastern	Kimutwa/Machakos	LJGM
9134	JM 2381	KEN	Eastern	Kimutwa/Machakos	LJGM
9135	JM 2383	KEN	Eastern	Kimutwa/Machakos	LJGM
9136	JM 2384	KEN	Eastern	Kimutwa/Machakos	LJGM
9137	JM 2385	KEN	Eastern	Wanazau/Machakos	LJGM
9138	JM 2387	KEN	Eastern	Wanazau/Machakos	LJGM
9139	JM 2388	KEN	Eastern	Kiou/Machakos	LJGM
9140	JM 2389	KEN	Eastern	Kiou/Machakos	LJGM
9141	JM 2391	KEN	Eastern	Sultanhamud/Machakos	LJGM
9142	JM 2392	KEN	Eastern	Sultanhamud/Machakos	LJGM
9143	JM 2395	KEN	Eastern	Sultanhamud/Machakos	LJGM
9144	JM 2396	KEN	Eastern	Sultanhamud/Machakos	LJGM
9145	JM 2397	KEN	Eastern	Sultanhamud/Machakos	LJGM
9146	JM 2398	KEN	Eastern	Sultanhamud/Machakos	LJGM
9147	JM 2400	KEN	Eastern	Muangan/Machakos	LJGM
9148	JM 2404	KEN	Eastern	Muangan/Machakos	LJGM
9149	JM 2409	KEN	Eastern	Ithanzu/Machakos	LJGM
9150	JM 2412	KEN	Eastern	Makueni/Machakos	LJGM
9151	JM 2413	KEN	Eastern	Makueni/Machakos	LJGM
9152	JM 2414	KEN	Eastern	Katangini/Machakos	LJGM
9153	JM 2415	KEN	Eastern	Ngungi-Kibaoni/Machakos	LJGM
9154	JM 2416	KEN	Eastern	Yathiwe/Machakos	LJGM
9155	JM 2418	KEN	Eastern	Miu/Machakos	LJGM
9156	JM 2419	KEN	Eastern	Miu/Machakos	LJGM
9157	JM 2420	KEN	Eastern	Ukia/Machakos	LJGM

Continued

Table 70 *Continued*

ICP No.	Pedigree	Country[1]	Province/ State	Location	Collector/ Donor
9158	JM 2421	KEN	Eastern	Majani/Machakos	LJGM
9159	JM 2423	KEN	Eastern	Majani/Machakos	LJGM
9173	JM 2464	KEN	Eastern	Kisasi/Kitui	
9174	JM 2467	KEN	Eastern	Kisasi/Kitui	LJGM
9175	JM 2470	KEN	Eastern	Chuluni/Kitui	LJGM
9176	JM 2471	KEN	Eastern	Kyambuswa/Kitui	LJGM
9177	JM 2472	KEN	Eastern	Kyambuswa/Kitui	LJGM
9179	JM 2476	KEN	Central	Mwea/Kirinyaga	LJGM
9180	JM 2477	KEN	Central	Mwea/Kirinyaga	LJGM
9181	JM 2478	KEN	Central	Kaharatha/Muranga	LJGM
9182	JM 2481	KEN	Rift Valley	Angogo-awasi/Kisumu	LJGM
9183	JE 2486	KEN	Rift Valley	Kisumu/Kisumu	LJGM
9184	JM 2488	KEN	Rift Valley	Kisumu/Kisumu	LJGM
9185	JM 2489	KEN	Rift Valley	Kisumu/Kisumu	LJGM
9186	JM 2490	KEN	Rift Valley	Kisumu/Kisumu	LJGM
9187	JM 2496	KEN	Rift Valley	Kibos/Kisumu	LJGM
9188	JM 2497	KEN	Rift Valley	Miwani/Kisumu	LJGM
9189	JM 2499	KEN	Rift Valley	Kibigori/Kisumu	LJGM
9190	JM 2504	KEN	Rift Valley	Chemilil/Kisumu	LJGM
9191	JM 2508	KEN	Rift Valley	Kisumu/Kisumu	LJGM
9192	JM 2510	KEN	Rift Valley	Ahero/Kisumu	LJGM
10003	JM 3497	IND	Kerala	17 km N of Kumali/Udiki	LJGM
10877	JM 2501	KEN	Rift Valley	Chemilil/Kisumu	
11887	JM 4295	IND	Uttar Pradesh	6 km of Mussoorie/Dehra Dun	LJGM
11892	JM 4343	IND	Uttar Pradesh	Pauri/Garhwal	LJGM
11895	JM 4365	IND	Uttar Pradesh	Chamoli/Chamoli	LJGM
11896	JM 4384	IND	Uttar Pradesh	Geodwa/Chamoli	LJGM

Continued

Table 70 *Continued*

ICP No.	Pedigree	Country[1]	Province/ State	Location	Collector/ Donor
11897	JM 4394	IND	Uttar Pradesh	Khanhar/Almora	LJGM
11980	PR 5265	PHL	–[2]	Tublay	PR
11981	PR 5266	PHL	–	Atok	PR
11982	PR 5267	PHL	–	Atok	PR
11983	PR 5268	PHL	–	Atok	PR
11984	PR 5271	PHL	–	Sabangan/Pingad	PR
12008	PR 5358	TZA	Iringa	Tanongozi/Iringa	PR
12009	PR 5360	TZA	Iringa	Ifunda/Iringa	PR
12011	PR 5367	TZA	Mbeya	Mbuyuni/Mbeya	PR
12012	PR 5368	TZA	Mbeya	Mbuyuni/Mbeya	PR
12071	PR 5446	TZA	Arusha	Kilimimoza/Mbulu	PR
12072	PR 5447	TZA	Mbeya	Kilimimoza/Mbeya	PR
12073	PR 5448	TZA	Arusha	Bashai/Mbulu	PR
12074	PR 5449	TZA	Arusha	Mizungu/Hanang	PR
12075	PR 5451	TZA	Mbeya	Mizungu/Mbeya	PR
12080	PR 5458	TZA	Arusha	Singe/Hanang	PR
12081	PR 5459	TZA	Arusha	Singe/Hanang	PR
12084	PR 5464	TZA	Dodoma	Saranka Karasini/Kondoa	PR
12085	PR 5465	TZA	Dodoma	Saranka Karasini/Kondoa	PR
12086	PR 5466	TZA	Dodoma	Saranka Karasini/Kondoa	PR
12087	PR 5467-1	TZA	Dodoma	Masavi/Kondoa	PR
12088	PR 5467-2	TZA	Dodoma	Masavi/Kondoa	PR
12089	PR 5468	TZA	Dodoma	Masavi/Kondoa	PR
12090	PR 5469	TZA	Dodoma	Kolo/Kondoa	PR
12091	PR 5470	TZA	Dodoma	Kolo/Kondoa	PR
12092	PR 5471	TZA	Dodoma	Kolo/Kondoa	PR
12093	PR 5472	TZA	Dodoma	Kolo/Kondoa	PR

Continued

Table 70 *Continued*

ICP No.	Pedigree	Country[1]	Province/ State	Location	Collector/ Donor
12094	PR 5474	TZA	Dodoma	Wisikwantisi/Kondoa	PR
12095	PR 5475	TZA	Dodoma	Wisikwantisi/Kondoa	PR
12096	PR 5476	TZA	Dodoma	Wisikwantisi/Kondoa	PR
12097	PR 5478-1	TZA	Dodoma	Sairia/Kondoa	PR
12098	PR 5478-2	TZA	Dodoma	Sairia/Kondoa	PR
12099	PR 5479	TZA	Dodoma	Sairia/Kondoa	PR
12100	PR 5480	TZA	Dodoma	Sairia/Kondoa	PR
12101	PR 5481	TZA	Dodoma	Sairia/Kondoa	PR
12102	PR 5482	TZA	Dodoma	Sairia/Kondoa	PR
12103	PR 5483	TZA	Dodoma	Sairia/Kondoa	PR
12104	PR 5485	TZA	Dodoma	Sairia/Kondoa	PR
12105	PR 5486-1	TZA	Dodoma	Bicha/Kondoa	PR
12106	PR 5486-2	TZA	Dodoma	Bicha/Kondoa	PR
12107	PR 5487	TZA	Dodoma	Balai/Kondoa	PR
12108	PR 5489-1	TZA	Dodoma	Kambianyasa/Kondoa	PR
12109	PR 5489-2	TZA	Dodoma	Kambianyasa/Kondoa	PR
12110	PR 5490	TZA	Dodoma	Kidoka/Kondoa	PR
12112	PR 5492	TZA	Dodoma	Zambeka/Kondoa	PR
12113	PR 5494	TZA	Dodoma	Miyugi/Dodoma	PR
12114	PR 5495	TZA	Dodoma	Miyugi/Dodoma	PR
12115	PR 5501	TZA	Dodoma	Manjali/Dodoma	PR
12116	PR 5502	TZA	Dodoma	Manjali/Dodoma	PR
12117	PR 5503	TZA	Dodoma	Kisokwe/Mpwapwa	PR
12118	PR 5504	TZA	Dodoma	Kisokwe/Mpwapwa	PR
12119	PR 5505	TZA	Dodoma	Kisokwe/Mpwapwa	PR
12120	PR 5506	TZA	Dodoma	Kisokwe/Mpwapwa	PR
12121	PR 5507	TZA	Dodoma	Masai/Mpwapwa	PR

Continued

Table 70 *Continued*

ICP No.	Pedigree	Country[1]	Province/ State	Location	Collector/ Donor
12122	PR 5510	TZA	Dodoma	Manakiyanga/Mpwapwa	PR
12123	PR 5513	TZA	Dodoma	Mtanam/Mpwapwa	PR
12124	PR 5514	TZA	Dodoma	Mtanam/Mpwapwa	PR
12125	PR 5517	TZA	Dodoma	Kibaigwa/Mpwapwa	PR
12126	PR 5518	TZA	Dodoma	Kibaigwa/Mpwapwa	PR
12127	PR 5519	TZA	Dodoma	Kibaigwa/Mpwapwa	PR
12128	PR 5520	TZA	Dodoma	Kibaigwa/Mpwapwa	PR
12129	PR 5521	TZA	Dodoma	Kibaigwa/Mpwapwa	PR
12130	PR 5522	TZA	Dodoma	Kibaigwa/Mpwapwa	PR
12131	PR 5523	TZA	Dodoma	Kibaigwa/Mpwapwa	PR
12132	PR 5524	TZA	Dodoma	Kibaigwa/Mpwapwa	PR
12133	PR 5525	TZA	Dodoma	Kibaigwa/Mpwapwa	PR
12134	PR 5526	TZA	Morogoro	Pandambili/Kilosa	PR
12135	PR 5527	TZA	Morogoro	Pandambili/Kilosa	PR
12136	PR 5529	TZA	Morogoro	Makambini/Kilosa	PR
12137	PR 5530	TZA	Morogoro	Makambini/Kilosa	PR
12138	PR 5531	TZA	Morogoro	Makambini/Kilosa	PR
12139	PR 5532	TZA	Dodoma	Kibaigwa/Mpwapwa	PR
12140	PR 5533	TZA	Dodoma	Kibaigwa/Mpwapwa	PR
12141	PR 5534	TZA	Dodoma	Kibaigwa/Mpwapwa	PR
12142	PR 5535	TZA	Morogoro	Dumila/Kilosa	PR
12143	PR 5537	TZA	Morogoro	Dumila/Kilosa	PR
12144	PR 5538	TZA	Morogoro	Dumila/Kilosa	PR
12145	PR 5539	TZA	Morogoro	Dumila/Kilosa	PR
12146	PR 5540	TZA	Morogoro	Dumila/Kilosa	PR
12147	PR 5541	TZA	Morogoro	Dumila/Kilosa	PR
12148	PR 5542	TZA	Morogoro	Dumila/Kilosa	PR
12149	PR 5543	TZA	Morogoro	Dumila/Kilosa	PR

Continued

Table 70 *Continued*

ICP No.	Pedigree	Country[1]	Province/State	Location	Collector/Donor
12150	PR 5544	TZA	Morogoro	Dumila/Kilosa	PR
12151	PR 5546	TZA	Morogoro	Magubike/Kilosa	PR
12165	PR 5574	TZA	Pwani	Near Dar es Salaam/Dar es Salaam	PR
12782	PR 5364	TZA	Morogoro	Ilonga/Kilosa	PR
12783	PR 5366	TZA	Mbeya	Mbuyuni/Mbeya	PR
12800	PR 5444	TZA	Arusha	Orari/Hai	PR
12802	PR 5452	TZA	Arusha	Mada/Hanang	PR
12805	PR 5473	TZA	Dodoma	Kontusi/Kondoa	PR
12806	PR 5477	TZA	Dodoma	Sairia/Kondoa	PR
12807	PR 5484	TZA	Dodoma	Minigani/Kondoa	PR
12810	PR 5497	TZA	Dodoma	Dodoma/Dodoma	PR
12811	PR 5499	TZA	Dodoma	Dodoma/Dodoma	PR
12812	PR 5509	TZA	Dodoma	Manakiyanga/Mpwapwa	PR
12813	PR 5511	TZA	Dodoma	Manakiyanga/Mpwapwa	PR
12814	PR 5515	TZA	Dodoma	Mtanana/Mpwapwa	PR
12816	PR 5528	TZA	Dodoma	Pandambili/Mpwapwa	PR
12817	PR 5536	TZA	Morogoro	Dumila/Kilosa	PR
12818	PR 5545	TZA	Morogoro	Magubike/Kilosa	PR
12819	PR 5547	TZA	Morogoro	Magubike/Kilosa	PR
13051	PRN 23	KEN	Eastern	Kitani/Kitui	PRN
13052	PRN 25	KEN	Eastern	Kakumati/Kitui	PRN
13053	PRN 26	KEN	Eastern	Matinyani/Kitui	PRN
13054	PRN 31	KEN	Eastern	Kyangunga/Kitui	PRN
13055	PRN 33	KEN	Eastern	Ilamba/Kitui	PRN
13056	PRN 35	KEN	Eastern	Ndambani/Kitui	PRN
13057	PRN 37	KEN	Eastern	Gitambangi/Kitui	PRN
13058	PRN 40	KEN	Eastern	Kothukiini/Kitui	PRN
13059	PRN 41	KEN	Eastern	Kwa-mali/Kitui	PRN

Continued

Table 70 *Continued*

ICP No.	Pedigree	Country[1]	Province/ State	Location	Collector/ Donor
13060	PRN 43	KEN	Eastern	Katulani/Kitui	PRN
13061	PRN 44	KEN	Eastern	Kisasi/Kitui	PRN
13062	PRN 45	KEN	Eastern	Kisasi/Kitui	PRN
13063	PRN 48	KEN	Eastern	Thandini/Kitui	PRN
13073	PRN 66-1	KEN	Eastern	Kalia/Kitui	PRN
13074	PRN 67	KEN	Eastern	Kalia/Kitui	PRN
13075	PRN 68	KEN	Eastern	Kalia/Kitui	PRN
13076	PRN 69	KEN	Eastern	Kathivo/Kitui	PRN
13077	PRN 70	KEN	Eastern	Kabati/Kitui	PRN
13078	PRN 75	KEN	Eastern	Kangonde/Machakos	PRN
13079	PRN 84	KEN	Eastern	Kanjatari/Embu	PRN
13089	PRN 103	KEN	Eastern	Chogoria/Meru	PRN
13090	PRN 112-1	KEN	Central	Kagio/Kirinyaga	PRN
13091	PRN 112-2	KEN	Central	Kagio/Kirinyaga	PRN
13092	PRN 113	KEN	Central	Kagio/Kirinyaga	PRN
13093	PRN 120	KEN	Central	Kangongu/Kirinyaga	PRN
13094	PRN 121-1	KEN	Central	Mugaa/Kirinyaga	PRN
13095	PRN 121-2	KEN	Central	Mugaa/Kirinyaga	PRN
13096	PRN 122	KEN	Central	Mutithi/Kirinyaga	PRN
13097	PRN 123	KEN	Central	Makutano/Kirinyaga	PRN
13098	PRN 125	KEN	Central	Makutano/Kirinyaga	PRN
13099	PRN 127	KEN	Central	Makutano/Kirinyaga	PRN
13100	PRN 130	KEN	Eastern	Mbubuni/Machakos	PRN
13101	PRN 131	KEN	Eastern	Usalala/Machakos	PRN
13102	PRN 133	KEN	Eastern	Kilungu/Machakos	PRN
13103	PRN 134	KEN	Eastern	Kilungu/Machakos	PRN
13104	PRN 135	KEN	Eastern	Kilungu/Machakos	PRN
13105	PRN 136	KEN	Eastern	Kilungu/Machakos	PRN
13106	PRN 140	KEN	Eastern	Makueni/Machakos	PRN

Continued

Table 70 *Continued*

ICP No.	Pedigree	Country[1]	Province/ State	Location	Collector/ Donor
13107	PRN 141	KEN	Eastern	Chamoli/Machakos	PRN
13108	PRN 143	KEN	Eastern	Chamoli/Machakos	PRN
13109	PRN 144	KEN	Eastern	Kathonzueni/Machakos	PRN
13110	PRN 146	KEN	Eastern	Kavumbu/Machakos	PRN
13111	PRN 153	KEN	Eastern	Sengelela/Machakos	PRN
13112	PRN 154	KEN	Eastern	Kibwezi/Machakos	PRN
13117	PRN 191	KEN	Eastern	Mutondoni/Machakos	PRN
13118	PRN 192	KEN	Eastern	Kathyani/Machakos	PRN
13119	PRN 193	KEN	Eastern	Kathyani/Machakos	PRN
13120	PRN 195	KEN	Eastern	Kathyani/Machakos	PRN
13121	PRN 197	KEN	Eastern	Chvaluki/Machakos	PRN
13122	PRN 206	KEN	Eastern	Kinani/Machakos	PRN
13123	PRN 207	KEN	Eastern	Kitani/Machakos	PRN
13124	PRN 209	KEN	Eastern	Kithangaini/Machakos	PRN
13125	PRN 210	KEN	Eastern	Kaani/Machakos	PRN
13126	PRN 211	KEN	Eastern	Mumoni/Machakos	PRN
13127	PRN 212	KEN	Eastern	Maasi/Machakos	PRN
13128	PRN 213	KEN	Eastern	Massi/Machakos	PRN
13129	PRN 214	KEN	Eastern	Kingtwani/Machakos	PRN
13130	PRN 215	KEN	Eastern	Embwe/Machakos	PRN
13131	PRN 216	KEN	Eastern	Mbaani/Machakos	PRN
13132	PRN 217-1	KEN	Eastern	Mbaani/Machakos	PRN
13133	PRN 217-2	KEN	Eastern	Mbaani/Machakos	PRN
13134	PRN 218	KEN	Eastern	Koineyni/Machakos	PRN
13135	PRN 219	KEN	Eastern	Kangethe/Machakos	PRN
13136	PRN 220	KEN	Eastern	Keyotheo/Machakos	PRN
13137	PRN 221	KEN	Eastern	Mutheteni/Machakos	PRN
13138	PRN 222	KEN	Eastern	Milatheni/Machakos	PRN

Continued

Table 70 *Continued*

ICP No.	Pedigree	Country[1]	Province/ State	Location	Collector/ Donor
13139	PRN 223	KEN	Eastern	Kaewa/Machakos	PRN
13140	PRN 224	KEN	Eastern	Ndithini/Machakos	PRN
13141	PRN 225	KEN	Eastern	Ndithini/Machakos	PRN
13142	PRN 226	KEN	Eastern	Musioka/Machakos	
13143	PRN 227	KEN	Eastern	Tawa/Machakos	PRN
13144	PRN 228	KEN	Eastern	Kiluku/Machakos	PRN
13145	PRN 232	KEN	Eastern	Kwajend/Machakos	PRN
13146	PRN 233	KEN	Eastern	Jani/Machakos	PRN
13147	PRN 234	KEN	Eastern	Katumani/Machakos	PRN
13148	PRN 235-1	KEN	Eastern	Katumani/Machakos	PRN
13149	PRN 235-2	KEN	Eastern	Katumani/Machakos	PRN
13150	PRN 236	KEN	Eastern	Katumani/Machakos	PRN
13151	PRN 237	KEN	Eastern	Kola/Machakos	PRN
13152	PRN 239	KEN	Eastern	Saakavi/Machakos	PRN
13153	PRN 240-2	KEN	Eastern	Ngele/Machakos	PRN
13154	PRN 241	KEN	Eastern	Okia/Machakos	PRN
13155	PRN 242	KEN	Eastern	Okia/Machakos	PRN
13156	PRN 243	KEN	Eastern	Etumbale/Machakos	PRN
13157	PRN 245	KEN	Eastern	Ukia/Machakos	PRN
13158	PRN 246	KEN	Eastern	Kiuva/Machakos	PRN
13159	PRN 247	KEN	Eastern	Makueni/Machakos	PRN
13160	PRN 249	KEN	Eastern	Nzueni/Machakos	PRN
13161	PRN 250	KEN	Eastern	Kilili/Machakos	PRN
13162	PRN 252	KEN	Eastern	Wee/Machakos	PRN
13163	PRN 253	KEN	Eastern	Kavale/Machakos	PRN
13164	PRN 254	KEN	Eastern	Thuwani/Machakos	PRN
13165	PRN 255	KEN	Eastern	Matiliku/Machakos	PRN

Continued

Table 70 *Continued*

ICP No.	Pedigree	Country[1]	Province/ State	Location	Collector/ Donor
13166	PRN 257	KEN	Eastern	Kaathi/Machakos	PRN
13167	PRN 259-1	KEN	Eastern	Sultanhamud Road/Machakos	PRN
13168	PRN 260	KEN	Eastern	Sultanhamud Road/Machakos	PRN
13169	PRN 261	KEN	Eastern	Muwani/Machakos	PRN
13170	PRN 262	KEN	Eastern	Kwamabu/Machakos	PRN
13171	PRN 264	KEN	Eastern	Kitandi/Machakos	PRN
13172	PRN 265	KEN	Eastern	Kitandi/Machakos	PRN
13173	PRN 267	KEN	Eastern	Kee/Machakos	PRN
13174	PRN 268	KEN	Eastern	Kee/Machakos	PRN
13175	PRN 271	KEN	Eastern	Kyanguli/Machakos	PRN
13176	PRN 272	KEN	Eastern	Kaviuni/Machakos	PRN
13177	PRN 278-1	KEN	Eastern	Mututani/Machakos	PRN
13178	PRN 282	KEN	Eastern	Kietini/Machakos	PRN
13179	PRN 283	KEN	Eastern	Kietini/Machakos	PRN
13180	PRN 285	KEN	Eastern	Kalama/Machakos	PRN
13181	PRN 286	KEN	Eastern	Miyani/Machakos	PRN
13182	PRN 288	KEN	Eastern	Utangwa/Machakos	PRN
13183	PRN 289-1	KEN	Eastern	Utangwa/Machakos	PRN
13184	PRN 291	KEN	Eastern	Kikima/Machakos	PRN
13185	PRN 292	KEN	Eastern	Kikima/Machakos	PRN

1. IND = India, KEN = Kenya, PHL = The Philippines, TZA = Tanzania.

2. = Unknown.

3. A complete list of these initials is given in the companion volume — ICRISAT Pigeonpea Germplasm Catalog: Passport Information.

Genetic stocks with unique traits

The gene bank maintains various genetic stocks which are useful in carrying out genetic studies, estimation of outcrossing, breeding of dwarfs, production of hybrids etc.

Genetic dwarfs. Early maturing lines appear as dwarfs when grown in a favorable environment (page 26), but are not real dwarfs. Genetic dwarfs (Plates 6 and 9) are rare in the world collection. Some dwarfs developed at ICRISAT include:
ICP 11975 (D0), 10961 (D1), 10962 (D2), 13950 (D3), 13951 (D4), 13952 (D5), 13953 (D6), and 13954 (D7).

Markers. Purple stem (Plate 3) (dominant over green) ICP 9150 (Table 29 gives more sources).
Retuse leaflet (recessive over normal) ICP 5529 (Fig. 6).

Genetic male-steriles.   ICP 11762 (MS 3 A)   (MS BDN 1)
                             ICP 11763 (MS 4 A)   (MS PS 66)

Many converted standard cultivars of different maturity groups are also available.

Mutants. Minute leaflet and two seeds per pod ICP 9880 (Fig. 6)
Sesamum leaflet ICP 9879 (Fig. 6)
Ovate leaflet ICP 5357 (Fig. 6)
Simple leaf, selection from ICP 8001 (Plate 7)
Minute seeds (2.8 g 100^{-1}) ICP 11947 (Plate 4).

Modified flowers. The cleistogamous condition found in T 21 × A. lineata derivatives (ICP 13695) ensures complete self-fertilization (ICRISAT 1982a). Modified flowers which inhibit cross-fertilization under Australian environment has been reported in the wrapped flowers of cultivar Royes (Byth et al. 1982). However, subsequent work has revealed that this may not apply under other environments (Saxena et al. 1987).

Accessions with 8-9 seeds per pod. ICP 8503, 8504 (origin: Guadeloupe), 12176 (origin: Malawi), 13253, 13256 (origin: Kenya), 13555, 13828, 13831 (origin: Grenada), and ICP 13961, 13962 (origin: Domini-

can Republic). ICP 8504 is a widely used breeding line while the others are recently identified sources. They originate from diverse geographical areas and differ in other morphological traits. Hence, the genetic base of cultivars with a high number of seeds per pod is now fairly wide.

Closely Related Wild Species

In presenting the status of genetic resources activities on wild relatives, Remanandan (1981) projected with specific examples the use of exotic germplasm to generate more variability in pigeonpea, such as building resistance against pests and diseases, and upgrading nutritional value.

Pigeonpea belongs to the subtribe *Cajaninae* which contains 13 genera. *Atylosia* (Plate 10) is the closest genus and *A. cajanifolia* is the most probable progenitor of pigeonpea. Many species of *Atylosia* cross readily with pigeonpea. Introgressed and backcrossed progenies of the following *Atylosia* species with various elite pigeonpea parents are now held in our collection. Small quantities of seed can be shared with other scientists.

Atylosia acutifolia F.V. Muell.	*A. pluriflora* F.V. Muell.
A. albicans (W. & A.) Benth.	*A. reticulata* (Dryander) Benth.
A. cajanifolia Haines.	*A. scarabaeoides* (L.) Benth.
A. lanceolata W.V. Fitzg.	*A. sericea* Benth.
A. latisepala Reynolds and Pedley.	*A. trinervia* (DC.) Gamble.
A. lineata W. & A.	

The present collection of wild relatives consists of 271 accessions of 47 species belonging to 6 genera. They have been evaluated for a few important traits and have been subjected to screening against diseases and pests. A remarkable trait of these wild species is that most of them have high seed protein (Table 71). The maximum recorded is 33.4% for *Atylosia mollis*, while the mean protein in pigeonpea is 22.1%.

Table 71. Some characteristics of wild species related to pigeonpea.

Species	No. of accessions	Days to 50% flowering	Growth habit[1]	100-seed mass (g)	Protein (%)	Remarks
Atylosia acutifolia (F.V. Muell. Reynolds and Pedley)	6	-	SS	2.4	-	-
A. albicans (W. & A). Benth.	14	510	CL	2.4	28.7	Sterility mosaic (SM) resistant, blight and podfly susceptible, high seed protein content, high trypsin and chymotrypsin inhibition
A. cajanifolia Haines.	4	118	ES	5.0	29.2	Highly susceptible to SM, blight-susceptible, susceptible to lepidopteran borers
A. goensis F.V. Muell. ex. Benth.	1	222	CL	3.2	-	-
A. lanceolata W.V. Fitz.	2	84	SS	3.7	-	-
A. latisepala Reynolds and Pedley	1	263	-	3.2	-	-
A. lineata W. & A.	10	188	SS	2.4	32.6	SM resistant, blight susceptible, high seed protein content
A. mareebensis Reynolds and Pedley	2	-	-	-	-	-
A. marmorata Benth.	1	90	CL	5.8	-	-
A. mollis Benth.	8	418	CL	1.9	33.4	High seed protein content
A. platycarpa Benth.	13	48	CR	4.5	29.3	Blight resistant SM susceptible, high seed protein content

Continued

Table 71 *Continued*

Species	No. of accessions	Days to 50% flowering	Growth habit[1]	100-seed mass (g)	Protein (%)	Remarks
A. pluriflora F. Muell. ex. Benth.	1	-	-	-	-	-
A. reticulata (Dryander) Benth.	5	188	SS	1.5	24.1	Exists in erect and twining forms
A. rugosa W. & A.	3	-	CR	1.6	-	-
A. scarabaeoides (L.) Benth.	45	82	CR	1.8	28.5	Varying degrees of susceptibility to SM and blight, *Hymenoptera* susceptible, Antibiosis to *Heliothis armigera*, high seed protein content
A. sericea Benth.	4	116	ES	1.8	28.6	Blight and SM resistant, susceptible to lepidopteran borers, high seed protein content
A. trinervia (DC.) Gamble	1	-	ES	-	-	-
A. volubilis (Blanco) Gamble	10	188	CL	3.5	29.1	SM resistant, blight susceptible, high seed protein content, high trypsin and chymotrypsin inhibition

Continued

Table 71 *Continued*

Species	No. of accessions	Days to 50% flowering	Growth habit[1]	100-seed mass (g)	Protein (%)	Remarks
Dunbaria ferruginea W. & A.	3	226	CL	3.4	-	-
D. heynei W. & A.	1	-	CL	5.2	-	-
Flemingia congesta Roxb.	3	215	SS	1.7	-	-
F. nana Roxb.	1	-	-	0.8	-	-
F. paniculata Will	1	-	SS	1.4	-	-
F. simialata Roxb.	1	-	SS	1.9	-	-
F. stricta Roxb.	1	-	SS	2.7	-	-
F. strobilifera (L.)Aiton	2	-	SS	1.3	-	-
Flemingia sp.	2	-	-	-	-	-
Paracalyx scariosa (Roxb.) Ali	3	168	CL	4.2	-	-
Rhynchosia hirta (Andrews) Meikle and Verdcourt	3	174	-	6.1	24.6	-
R. aurea DC.	4	40	CR	2.8	-	Annual
R. bracteata Benth. ex. Bak	3	181	CL	8.9	28.6	-
R. cana DC.	4	129	SS	2.6	30.7	-
R. densiflora DC.	2	137	-	1.5	26.4	-
R. filipes Benth.	2	232	TR	2.0	-	-
R. heynei W. & A.	1	-	TR	2.3	-	-
R. himalensis Bth. ex. Bak	1	-	-	-	-	-
R. melacophylla (Spreng.) Boj	1	95	-	0.9	-	-
R. minima DC.	3	45	CR	1.8	26.0	Annual
R. rothii Benth. ex. Aitch	9	80	CL	5.6	28.7	High seed protein content, extreme trypsin and chymotrypsin inhibition
R. rufescens DC.	3	159	TR	2.6	-	-
R. suaveolens DC.	1	106	SS	3.3	24.9	-
R. sublobata Meikle	2	110	CL	10.1	-	-
R. viscida DC.	2	108	-	4.9	28.4	-

1. CL = Climber, CR = Creeper, ES = Upright with erect stem, SS = Upright with semi-spreading habit, TR = Trailing habit.

Seed Distribution

One of the major responsibilities of ICRISAT is to act as a world repository for the genetic resources of its mandate crops. The world collection of pigeonpea assembled at ICRISAT from 52 countries is the largest pigeonpea collection assembled at one place. Crop genetic resources are man's priceless heritage and we believe this collection conserved at ICRISAT belongs to the whole world. ICRISAT supplies the germplasm free of charge to all scientists who wish to utilize it. This important service is handled by the Genetic Resources Unit of ICRISAT and it will have significant impact in the future as natural genetic diversity gradually diminishes throughout the world as elite materials replace landraces.

ICRISAT supplies only clean and viable seeds that have been inspected and cleared by the Quarantine authorities of the Government of India. All those who wish to obtain germplasm from ICRISAT may simply write to the Genetic Resources Unit and may use the proforma for seed request given in this catalog.

Anyone wishing to send seed samples to ICRISAT should send the samples accompanied by a phytosanitary certificate to:

The Director
National Bureau of Plant Genetic Resources
Pusa Campus
New Delhi 110 012, INDIA

The original phytosanitary certificate should be placed in an envelope affixed to the outside of the parcel. You are requested to use new envelopes for sending the seed to avoid contamination of seed.

Copies of the seed list, passport information of samples, phytosanitary certificate, and covering letter should be sent directly to GRU. We use the collection data form given in this catalog to record field data during collection. Those who send seed to ICRISAT may use it, although it is not compulsory to fill all the columns.

ICRISAT has so far exchanged pigeonpea germplasm with 90 countries and Table 72 summarizes germplasm distributed from 1974 to 31 March 1988.

Format for seed request with example

To

The Program Leader
Genetic Resources Unit
ICRISAT
Patancheru P.O.
Andhra Pradesh, 502 324, India

Please supply us the following seed samples:

Crop	: PIGEONPEA
Quantity	: 100 seeds per sample
No. of samples	: 50
Purpose	: Observation nursery
Location	: Machakos, Kenya
Latitude	: 1.5°S
Altitude	: 1500 m

Desired traits

1. Maturity	: VII to VIII gr.
2. Seed mass (g 100⁻¹ seeds)	: 12 to 15g
3. Seed color	: White, yellow white
4. Any other	: Wilt resistance

Need for import permit   Yes, enclosed [X]
Not needed [ ]

Postal address: NDFRC
Katumani, Machakos,
P.O. Box 340
KENYA

Table 72. Number of pigeonpea germplasm samples distributed by the Genetic Resources Unit, ICRISAT from 1974 to end March 1988.

Year	Within ICRISAT	In India	Outside India	Total
1974	-	14	156	170
1975	-	290	812	1 102
1976	1 081	3 498	1 961	6 540
1977	3 365	760	512	4 637
1978	5 459	1 203	41	6 703
1979	6 316	1 487	365	8 168
1980	7 845	1 213	531	9 589
1981	5 509	2 524	623	8 656
1982	6 858	1 356	569	8 783
1983	4 380	1 597	591	6 568
1984	3 467	1 164	452	5 083
1985	1 663	1 597	532	3 792
1986	4 818	1 888	1 160	7 866
1987	2 258	1 647	1 638	5 543
1988	1	54	125	180
Total	53 020	20 292	10 068	83 380

References

Abrams, R., and Julia, F.J. 1973. Effect of planting time, plant population and row spacing on yield and other characteristics of pigeonpeas, *Cajanus cajan* (L.) Millsp., University of Puerto Rico Journal of Agriculture 57: 275-285.

Ahlawat, I.P.S., Saraf, C.S., Patil, R.R., and Parshad Mahabir. 1981. Multiple correlations and regression studies in pigeonpea. Indian Journal of Agronomy 26: 432-434.

Akinola, J.O., Whiteman, P.C., and Wallis, E.S. 1975. Agronomy of the pigeonpea (*Cajanus cajan*). Review series No.1/1975. Commonwealth Bureau of Pastures and Field Crops, Maidenhead, UK.

Ariyanayagam, R.P. 1975. Status of research in pigeonpea in Trinidad. Pages 131-139. International Grain Legumes Workshop Proceedings., ICRISAT, Hyderabad, India. Patancheru, A.P. 502 324, India: International Crops Research Institute for the Semi-Arid Tropics.

Asawa, B.M., Chandra, R.K., and Panday, R.L. 1981. Character correlations and divergence in pigeonpea. Indian Journal of Agricultural Sciences 51(1): 12-17.

Bainiwal, C.R., and Jatasra, D.S. 1983. Component analysis in pigeonpea [*Cajanus cajan* (L.) Millsp.]. Indian Journal of Heredity 15: 1-5.

Balyan, H.S., and Sudhakar, M.V. 1985. Path coefficient studies in pigeonpea. International Pigeonpea Newsletter 4: 18-20. Patancheru, A.P. 502 324, India: International Crops Research Institute for the Semi-Arid Tropics.

Beohar, A.R.L., and Nigam, P.K. 1972. Correlation studies in arhar, *Cajanus cajan* (L.) Millsp. JNKVV Research Journal 6(1): 58.

Byth, D.E. 1981. Breeding. Pages 487-495 *in* Proceedings of the International Workshop on Pigeonpeas, Vol.1. 15-19 December 1980, ICRISAT, Hyderabad, India. Patancheru. A.P. 502 324, India: International Crops Research Institute for the Semi-Arid Tropics.

Byth, D.E., Saxena, K.B., and Wallis, E.S. 1982. A mechanism for inhibiting cross-fertilization in pigeonpea [*Cajanus cajan* (L.) Millsp.]. Euphytica 31: 405-408.

Byth, D.E., Wallis, E.S., and Saxena, K.B. 1981. Adaptation and Breeding strategies for Pigeonpea. Pages 450-465 *in* Proceedings of the International Workshop on Pigeonpeas. Vol.1. 15-19 December 1980, ICRISAT, Hyderabad, India. Patancheru. A.P. 502 324, India: International Crops Research Institute for the Semi-Arid Tropics.

Chandra, S., Asthana, A.N., Ali, M., Sachan, J.N., Lal,S.S., Singh, R.A. and Gangal, L.K. 1983. Pigeonpea cultivation in India – A Package of Practices. Project Directorate Pulses, ICAR, Kanpur 208 024.

Chang, T.T. 1976. Manual on Genetic Conservation of Rice Germplasm for Evaluation and Utilization. The International Rice Research Institute, Philippines. 77 pp.

Dahiya, B.S. 1980. An annotated bibliography of pigeonpea 1900-1977. ICRISAT, Hyderabad, India. Patancheru, A.P. 502 324, India: International Crops Research Institute for the Semi-Arid Tropics. 183 pp.

Dahiya, B.S., Brar, J.S., Bhardwaj, B.L., and Bajaj, R.K. 1978. Studies on the heritability and inter-relationship of some agronomically important characters in pigeonpea [Cajanus cajan (L.) Millsp.]. Genetica Agraria 32(3-4): 305-313.

Dasappa, and Mahadevappa, M. 1970. Investigations on grain yield and related characters of some tur varieties. Mysore Journal of Agricultural Science 4: 212-215.

D'Cruz, R., and Deokar, A.B. 1970. Genetic Studies in Pigeonpea I.N. Green x Red grained. Mahatma Phule Agricultural University Research Journal 1: 44-53.

Dumbre, A.D., Deshmukh, R.B., and Patil, J.V. 1985. Path analysis in pigeonpea. Legumes Research 8: 37-38.

El-Swaify, S.A., Pathak, P., Rego, T.J., and Singh, S. 1985. Soil Management for Optimized Productivity Under Rainfed Conditions in the Semi-Arid Tropics. Springer-Verlag New York, Inc. Advances in Soil Science, Volume 1: 1-64.

Ganguli, D.K., and Srivastava, D.P. 1972. Genotypic and phenotypic correlation studies in arhar [Cajanus cajan (L.) Millsp.]. Indian Agriculture 16(1): 109-111.

Gomez, K.A., and Gomez, A.A. 1976. Statistical procedures for agricultural research, with emphasis on rice. International Rice Research Institute, Los Baños, Philippines. 294 pp.

Govinda Raju, D.R., and Sharat Chandra, H.C. 1972. Studies on variability in tur. Andhra Agricultural Journal 9(5-6): 155-156.

Gupta, S.C., Saxena, K.B., and Sharma, D. 1981. Inheritance of days to flower and of seed size in pigeonpea. Pages 61-66 in Proceedings of the International Workshop on Pigeonpeas. Vol.2. 15-19 December 1980, ICRISAT, Hyderabad, India. Patancheru, A.P. 502 324, India. International Crops Research Institute for the Semi-Arid Tropics.

Hawkes, J.H. (In press). Theory and practice of collecting germplasm in a centre of diversity. International Symposium on the Conservation and Utilization of Ethiopian Germplasm. 13–16 October 1986, Addis Ababa: PGRC/E, Addis Ababa, Ethiopia.

Huda, A.K.S., and Virmani, S.M. 1987. Agroclimatic environment of chickpea and pigeonpea. Pages 28 and 29 in Adaptation of chickpea and pigeonpea to abiotic stresses. Proceedings of the Consultants' Workshop, 19-21 December 1984, ICRISAT Center, India. Patancheru, A.P. 502 324, India: ICRISAT.

ICRISAT (International Crops Research Institute for the Semi-Arid Tropics). 1975. Annual Report 1974/75. Patancheru, A.P. 502 324, India: ICRISAT. 87 pp.

ICRISAT (International Crops Research Institute for the Semi-Arid Tropics). 1976. Annual Report 1975/76. Patancheru, A.P. 502 324, India: ICRISAT. 233 pp.

ICRISAT (International Crops Research Institute for the Semi-Arid Tropics). 1977. Annual Report 1976/77. Patancheru, A.P. 502 324, India: ICRISAT. 239 pp.

ICRISAT (International Crops Research Institute for the Semi-Arid Tropics). 1978. Annual Report 1977/78. Patancheru, A.P. 502 324, India: ICRISAT. 295 pp.

ICRISAT (International Crops Research Institute for the Semi-Arid Tropics). 1979. Annual Report 1978/79. Patancheru, A.P. 502 324, India: ICRISAT. 288 pp.

ICRISAT (International Crops Research Institute for the Semi-Arid Tropics). 1982a. Annual Report 1981. Patancheru, A.P. 502 324, India: ICRISAT. 364 pp.

ICRISAT (International Crops Research Institute for the Semi-Arid Tropics). 1982b. ICRISAT in the eighties, a 10-year plan. Patancheru, A.P. 502 324, India: ICRISAT. 61 pp.

ICRISAT (International Crops Research Institute for the Semi-Arid Tropics). 1985. Annual Report 1984. Patancheru, A.P. 502 324, India: ICRISAT. 376 pp.

Kumar, A., and Haque, M.F. 1973. Variability and correlation studies in F$_2$ population of pigeonpea [Cajanus cajan (L.) Millsp.]. Mysore Journal of Agricultural Science 7: 174-183.

Kumar, A.S., and Reddy, P.T. 1982. Path coefficient analysis of yield attributes in pigeonpea [Cajanus cajan (L.) Millsp.]. Genetica Agraria 36: 63-72.

Malik, B.P.S., Paroda, R.S., and Chaudhary, B.D. 1981a. Partial correlation and path coefficient analysis of seed yield characters in pigeonpea. Pages 109-115 in Proceedings of the International Workshop on Pigeonpeas. Vol. 2. 15-19 December 1980, ICRISAT, Hyderabad, India. Patancheru, A.P. 502 324, India. International Crops Research Institute for the Semi-Arid Tropics.

Malik, B.P.S., Singh, V.P., Paroda, R.S., and Gupta, S.C. 1981b. Correlation and path coefficient analysis in pigeonpea. Crop Improvement 8: 100-105.

Mengesha, M.H. 1984. International germplasm collection, conservation, and exchange at ICRISAT. Crop Science of America, 677 South Segoe Road, Madison, WI. 53711.

Pandey, R.K., and Singh, V.B. 1981. Influence of source and sink size on flower drop and seed yield of pigeonpea. Indian Journal Agricultural Sciences 51: 185-188.

Pathak, G.N. (1970). Red gram in Pulse Crops of India (Ed. P. Kachroo), Indian Council of Agricultural Research, New Delhi.

Ramanujam, S. and Singh, S.P. 1981. Pigeonpea Breeding in the All India Coordinated Programme. Pages 403-414 in Proceedings of the International Workshop on Pigeonpeas. 15-19 December 1980, ICRISAT, Hyderabad, India. Vol. 1. Patancheru, A.P. 502 324, India: International Crops Research Institute for the Semi-Arid Tropics.

Remanandan, P. 1981. The Wild Genepool of Cajanus at ICRISAT, Present and Future. Pages 29-38 in Proceedings of the International Workshop on Pigeonpeas. 15-19 December 1980, ICRISAT, Hyderabad, India. Vol. 2. Patancheru, A.P. 502 324, India: International Crops Research Institute for the Semi-Arid Tropics.

Remanandan, P., Shakoor, A., and Ngugi, E.C.K. 1982. Pigeonpea germplasm collection mission in Kenya, Sept-Oct 1982. Genetic Resources Progress Report 48. Patancheru, A.P. 502 324, India: International Crops Research Institute for the Semi-Arid Tropics. 48 pp.

Saxena, K.B., Faris, D.G., and Vijaya Kumar, R. 1984. Report of work June 1983-May 1984. Pigeonpea Breeding Progress Report 7, ICRISAT, Hyderabad, India. Patancheru, A.P. 502 324, India: International Crops Research Institute for the Semi-Arid Tropics. 99 pp.

Saxena, K.B., Gupta, M.D., and Faris, D.G. 1983. Report on Latematuring Pigeonpea. Pigeonpea Breeding Progress Report 5, ICRISAT, Hyderabad, India. Patancheru, A.P. 502 324, India: International Crops Research Institute for the Semi-Arid Tropics. 80 pp.

Saxena, K.B., Sharma, D., and Faris, D.G. 1987. Ineffectiveness of wrapped flower in inhibiting cross-fertilization in pigeonpea at Hyderabad, India. Euphytica 36: 295-297.

Saxena, M.C., and Yadav, D.S. 1975. Some agronomic considerations of pigeonpeas and chickpeas. Pages 31-61 in Grain Legumes Workshop Proceedings., ICRISAT, Hyderabad, India. Patancheru, A.P. 502 324, India: International Crops Research Institute for the Semi-Arid Tropics.

Shakoor, A., Ngugi, E.C.K., Omanga, P.A., Muthoka, M.S., and Mihu, S.G. 1984. Development of drought-resistant, high-yielding pigeonpea lines suitable for semi-arid areas. East African Agricultural and Forestry Journal. Special Issue: 312-317.

Sharma, D., Reddy, L.J., Green, J.M., and Jain, K.C, 1981. International Adaptation of Pigeonpeas. Pages 71-81 in Proceedings of the International Workshop on Pigeonpeas. 15-19 December 1980, ICRISAT, Hyderabad, India. Vol. 1. Patancheru, A.P. 502 324, India: International Crops Research Institute for the Semi-Arid Tropics.

Sharma, H.K. 1981. Genetic analysis of plant height in pigeonpea. Pages 55-59 in Proceedings of the International Workshop on Pigeonpeas. Vol. 2. 15-19 December 1980, ICRISAT, Hyderabad, India. Patancheru, A.P. 502 324, India. International Crops Research Institute for the Semi-Arid Tropics.

Sheldrake, A.R. 1984. Pigeonpea. The Physiology of Tropical Field Crops. Edited by P.R. Goldsworthy and N.M. Fisher. John Wiley & Sons Ltd. 390 pp.

Sheldrake, A.R., Narayanan, A., and Venkataratnam, N. 1979. The effects of flower removal on the seed yield of pigeonpeas (Cajanus cajan). Annals of Applied Botany, 91: 383-390.

Sidhu, P.S., Verma, M.M., Cheema, H.S., and Sra, S.S. 1985. Genetic relationships among yield components in pigeonpea. Indian Journal of Agricultural Sciences 55: 232-235.

Singh, R.P., and Shrivastava, M.P. 1979. Co-heritability and path analysis of yield and its components in pigeonpea [Cajanus cajan (L.) Millsp.]. JNKVV Research Journal 13: 42-45.

Smithson, B. (in press.) Evaluation methods and utilization of germplasm of annual crop species. International Symposium on the Conservation and Utilization of Ethiopian Germplasm. 13–16 October 1986. Addis Ababa: PGRC/E, Addis Ababa, Ethiopia.

Swindale, L.D. 1982. Distribution and Use of Arable soils in the Semi-Arid Tropics. Managing Soil Resources. 12th International Congress of Soil Science, New Delhi. 8-16 February 1982.

Tayo, T.O. 1980. Compensatory growth and yield of pigeonpea (Cajanus cajan) following pod removal at different stages of reproductive growth. Journal of Agricultural Science, Cambridge, 95: 487-491.

Upadhaya, L.P., and Saharia, P. 1980. Interrelationship between yield and yield components in pigeonpea [Cajanus cajan (L.) Millsp.]. Research in Assam Agricultural University (1): 43-47.

van der Maesen, L.J.G. 1980. India is the native home of the pigeonpea. Miscellaneous Papers 19 (1980). Landbouwhogeschool, Wageningen.

Virmani, S.M., Sivakumar, M.V.K., and Reddy, S.J. 1980. Climatological features of the SAT in relation to the farming systems research program. Pages 5-16 In Proceedings of the International Workshop on the Agroclimatological Research Needs of the Semi-Arid Tropics, 22-24 Nov 1978, ICRISAT, Hyderabad, India. Patancheru, A.P. 502 324, India: ICRISAT.

Wakankar, S.M., and Yadav, L.N. 1975. Path analysis of yield components in arhar [Cajanus cajan (L.) Millsp.). Indian Journal of Agricultural Research 9(4): 182-186.